CUTTIN

GE

ELEMENTARY

WORKBOOK

peter moor sarah cunningham

Contents

module 1

Names and countries

1 **a)** Complete the conversation with words from the box.

~~My~~ this your Hello you name 's Nice And What

SEBASTIAN: Hello. (1) *My* .... name (2) .... Sebastian. (3) ....'s (4) .... name?

FLORENCE: My (5) ....'s Florence.

SEBASTIAN: (6) .... to meet (7) ...., Florence.

FLORENCE: (8) .... you.

SEBASTIAN: And (9) .... is my friend, Charlotte.

FLORENCE: Hello, Charlotte.

CHARLOTTE: (10) ....

b) Listen and repeat the conversation.

Personal information: *be*

2 Write the questions and answers.

a) Jim Carrey – USA

1 *What's his name?*
2 *His name's Jim Carrey.*
3 *Where's he from?*
4 *He's from the USA.*

b) Gisele Bundchen – Brazil

1 What ....?
2 Her ....
3 Where ....?
4 She ....

c) Andrea, Jim, Caroline and Sharon Corr – Ireland

1 What ....?
2 Their ....
3 Where ....?
4 They ....

d) Venus Williams – the USA

1 ....?
2 ....
3 ....?
4 ....

e) David and Victoria Beckham – England

1 ....?
2 ....
3 ....?
4 ....

f) Roberto Benigni – Italy

1 ....?
2 ....
3 ....?
4 ....

is or *are*

3 Complete the sentences with *is* or *are*.

a My name ..*is*.................. Martina.
b Where .... you from?
c .... Walter from Germany?
d He .... 22 years old.
e .... Ross and Jennifer married?
f .... you on holiday?
g Fernanda .... a Spanish teacher.

Negative sentences

4 Make the sentences negative.

a Edinburgh ~~is~~ isn't in England.
b I'm from Ireland.
c My mother and father are English.
d Brazil is a small country.
e My name is Lana.
f My sister is married.
g I'm 15 years old.
h Philip and Elizabeth are on holiday.

Personal questions: *be*

5 **a)** Choose a word from Column B to complete each question.

Column A	Column B
1 What's your ..*name*..............?	student
2 How are ....?	brothers
3 How old are your ....?	Michelle
4 Are you a ....?	English
5 Is David ....?	you
6 Is your name ....?	holiday
7 Where are they ....?	~~name~~
8 Are they on ....?	from

b) Listen to the questions on the recording. Practise saying them.

Short answers

6 Write the short answers for the questions.

a Are you Portuguese?
No, ..*I'm not*.................. . I'm Brazilian.
b Is James English?
Yes, ... He's from Manchester.
c Is your address 16 New Street?
No, ... It's 26 New Road.
d Are you and your friend here on holiday?
No, ... We're here on business.
e Is Barbara married?
Yes, ... Her husband's a doctor.
f Are you married?
Yes, ... This is my husband, James.
g Is Thomas an actor?
No, ... He's a musician.
h Are Anne and Michael English?
No, ... They're from Ireland.
i Is 'Howard' your surname?
Yes, ... My first name's Tony.
j Is Jacqueline a teacher?
No, ... She's a student.

Possessive adjectives

7 Look at the pictures and complete the sentences with *my*, *your*, *his*, *her*, *our* or *their*.

Hi! (a) *My*.................. name's Ed ... Ed Turner! And this is (b) .... wife. (c) .... name's Thelma. This is (d) .... beautiful house!!

This is Thelma with (e) .... two children – (f) .... names are Bob and Tracey – and (g) .... brother – (h) .... name's Louis.

And this is (i) .... dog ... what's (j) .... name, friend?

(k) .... name's Bones.

Indefinite article: *a(n)*

8 Write *a* or *an*.

a *an*............ actor
b .... manager
c .... e-mail address
d .... lesson
e .... telephone number
f .... holiday
g .... teacher
h .... English teacher

Vocabulary

Jobs

9 Rearrange the mixed-up letters to make words for jobs.

a racto *actor*...............
b raweit ....
c eclipo coiffer ....
d anumisic ....
e createh ....
f stonprams ....
g sittar ....
h rocdot ....

Vocabulary booster: countries and nationalities

10 **a)** Write the nationalities.

	Country	Nationality
1	Australia	*Australian*........
2	Brazil	....
3	Italy	....
4	England	....
5	Spain	....
6	Scotland	....
7	France	....
8	USA	....

b) Listen and practise saying the words.

Listen and read

11 Listen and read about four people.
Who:

a is an actress? *Béatrice Santini*
b is a taxi driver? ....
c is from France? ....
d are musicians? ....
e is from London? ....
f is from Edinburgh? ....
g is a bus driver? ....
h is 45 years old? ....

People from different places

Béatrice Santini

Béatrice Santini is from France. She's 28 years old, and she's an actress. She's married; her husband is film director, Karol Bolewski. Karol is 56 years old. Their home is in Paris.

Magnus Mills

'Hello. My name is Magnus Mills. I'm 37 years old, and I'm single. I'm a bus driver in London. I'm also a writer: my first book is *Bus Driver on Holiday*.'

Donna Fiorelli

Donna Fiorelli is from New York. She's a taxi driver. She's 45 years old. Is she married? 'Yes, I am ... I'm married to my job.'

Plankton

Allan, Doug, Richard and Kirsty are Plankton ... four musicians from Aberdeen, in Scotland. Their manager is Betty Booth. Betty is from Edinburgh, and she's 25 years old.

Punctuation: capital letters

LOOK!

We use capital letters for:

- names *Lara Croft*
- countries *China*
- nationalities *Brazilian*
- roads *Fifth Avenue*
- towns/cities *Istanbul*

12 Write the capital letters.

a his name's graham smith.
His name's Graham Smith.

b my mother's from the united states.
....

c are you spanish?
....

d our school is in camden road.
....

e i'm from rome.
....

f eric lives in berlin.
....

Improve your writing

Addresses in English

13 a) Look at the address on this envelope.

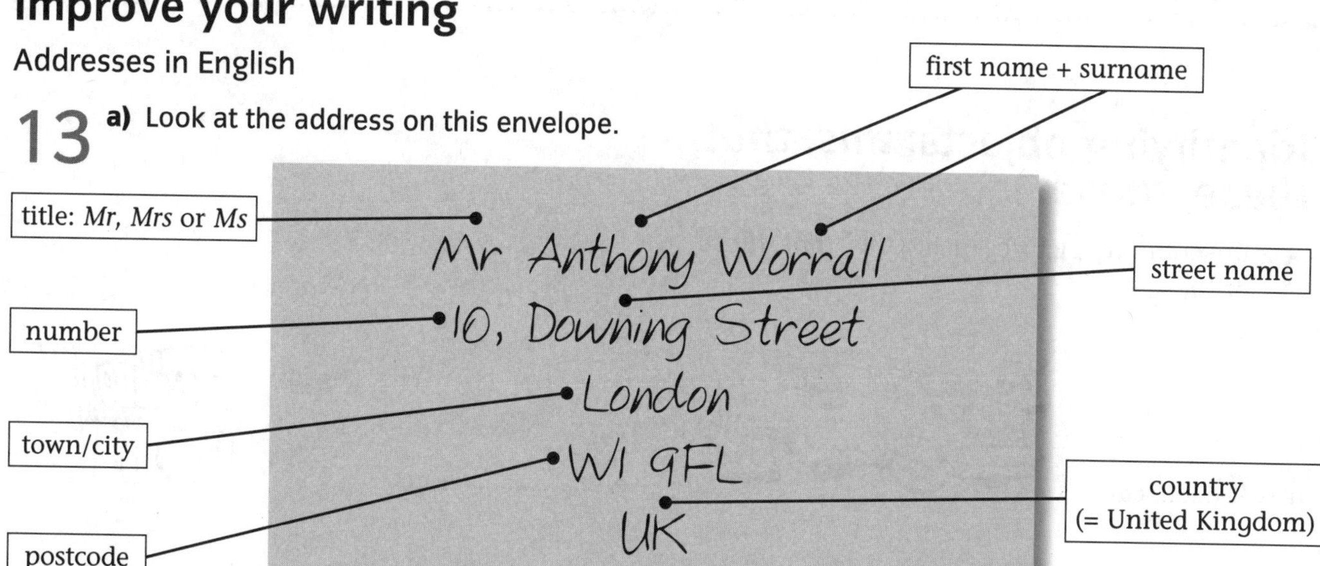

b) Write these addresses in the correct order.

1 SW15 6GS – South London College – UK – London – Richmond Road – 52

....

....

....

....

....

2 Dublin – 4 – Ireland – Mary Burke – Mrs – 109 St Stephen Street

....

....

....

....

....

c) Write the capital letters.

miss sarah ellis	....
62 high street	....
amersham	....
hp7 0dj	....
england	....

mr simon henderson	....
12 muirfield road	....
glasgow	....
g12 8sj	....
scotland	....

Pronunciation

/ɒ/, /eɪ/ and /aɪ/

14 a) Listen to the pronunciation of these words. Practise saying them.

/ɒ/	/eɪ/	/aɪ/
what	name	I
from	age	fine
holiday	they	my

b) Listen to the words. Write /ɒ/, /eɪ/ or /aɪ/.

1 write /.....aɪ...../
2 eight /............../
3 job /............../
4 doctor /............../
5 nine /............../
6 Spain /............../
7 nice /............../
8 not /............../

module 2

Identifying objects: *this*, *that*, *these*, *those*

1 Describe the pictures, using *this*, *that*, *these* or *those*.

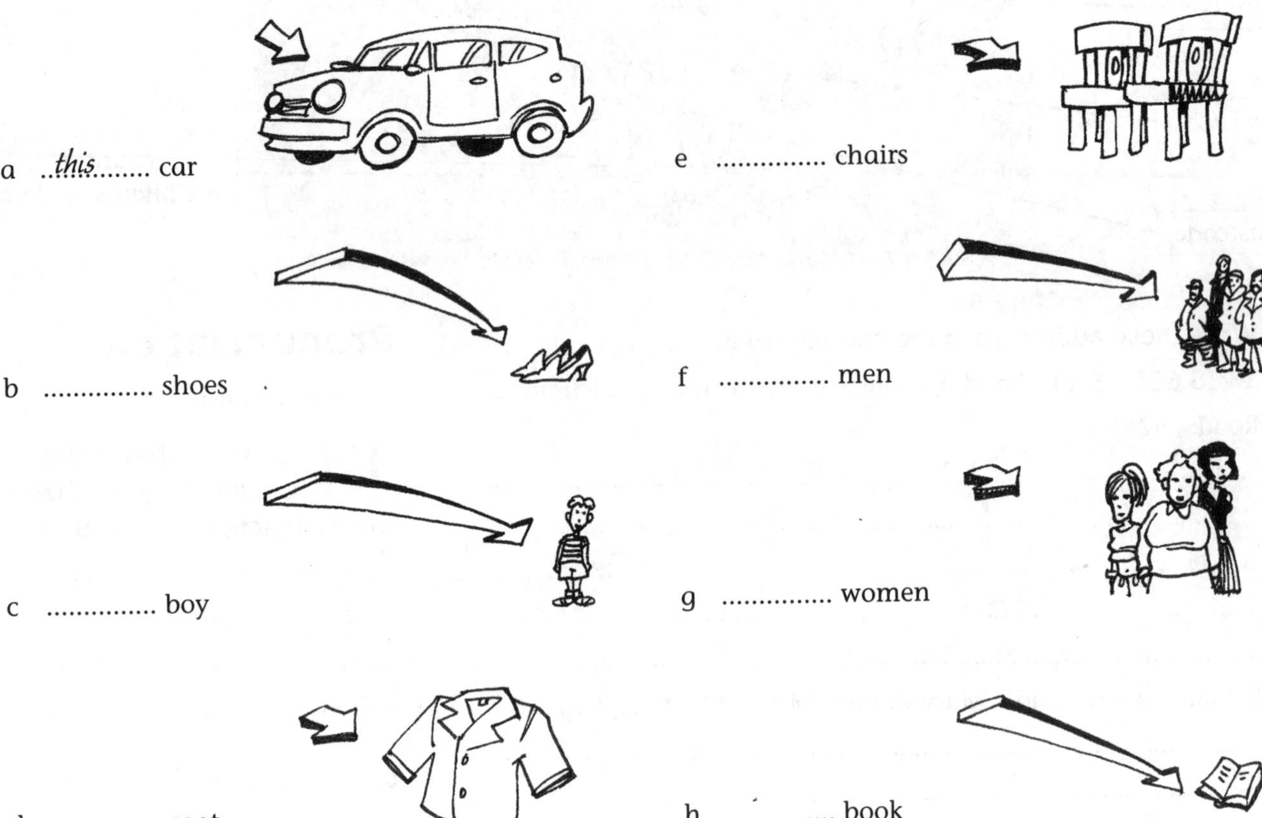

a ...*this*........ car

b .... shoes

c .... boy

d .... coat

e .... chairs

f .... men

g .... women

h .... book

a/*an* or Ø with objects and plurals

2 What's in the bag? Write *a*, *an*, or, Ø.

a ....*a*........ mobile phone

b .... apple

c .... English dictionary

d .... camera

e .... address book

f .... keys

g .... comb

h .... photos

i .... diary

j .... identity card

have/has got

3 **a)** Read the information in the table. Complete the sentences with *'s got*, *hasn't got*, *'ve got* or *haven't got*.

	Silvia	Martin and Inge	Alfonso
Pet?	dog (Rex)	no	two cats
Car?	yes – an Audi	two	no
Computer?	no	yes	yes

1 Silvia *'s got* a dog – his name's Rex.
2 She .... a car – it's an Audi.
3 She .... a computer.
4 Martin and Inge .... a pet.
5 They .... two cars.
6 They .... a computer.
7 Alfonso .... two cats.
8 He .... a car.
9 He .... a computer.

b) Listen and check your answers. Practise saying the sentences.

Questions and short answers

LOOK!

Have I/you/we/they **got**	a dog? a car?	**Yes**, I/you/we **have**. **No**, I/you/we **haven't**.
Has he/she/it **got**	a computer?	**Yes**, he/she/it **has**. **No**, he/she/it **hasn't**.

4 **a)** Look back at the information about Silvia, Alfonso and Martin and Inge and complete the questions and answers below.

1 *Has* Silvia *got* a dog?
Yes, she has.
2 .... she .... a car?
....
3 .... she .... a computer?
....
4 .... Martin and Inge .... a pet?
....
5 .... they .... a car?
....
6 .... they .... a computer?
....
7 .... Alfonso .... a pet?
....
8 .... he .... a car?
....
9 .... he .... a computer?
....

b) Listen and check your answers. Practise saying the sentences.

's = is or *has*?

5 **a)** In the paragraph below, *'s* is missing eight times. Write *'s* in the correct places.

My friend Steve's got a fantastic life, he only 21, but he got a great job – he a professional footballer – and he got lots of money. He got a new car, too – it a Porsche. It white, and it got everything, even a CD player!

b) Does 's = *is* or *has*?

1 *has* 5 ....
2 .... 6 ....
3 .... 7 ....
4 .... 8 ....

Adjectives and nouns

LOOK!

Adjectives:

- go **before** nouns	*a comfortable car*
- do **not** change	*blue eyes*
- do **not** use *and*	*a large red hat*

6 Put the adjective in the correct place in the sentences.

a Max has got a car – it's a BMW. (*German*)
Max has got a German car – it's a BMW. ....

b Your dog has got eyes. (*beautiful*)
....

c We've got two cats at home. (*black*)
....

d I've got a computer game – *Crash 5!!!* (*fantastic*)
....

e My friend Al is a musician. (*professional*)
....

f Lauren Bacall is my actress. (*favourite*)
....

g My sister's got a mobile phone. (*new*)
....

h Goldie is a dog. (*friendly*)
....

Vocabulary booster: more everyday objects

7 **a)** Label the objects in the picture with words from the box.

a passport an address book a hairbrush car keys a calculator a pen a pencil a mirror a tube of lipstick a packet of chewing gum

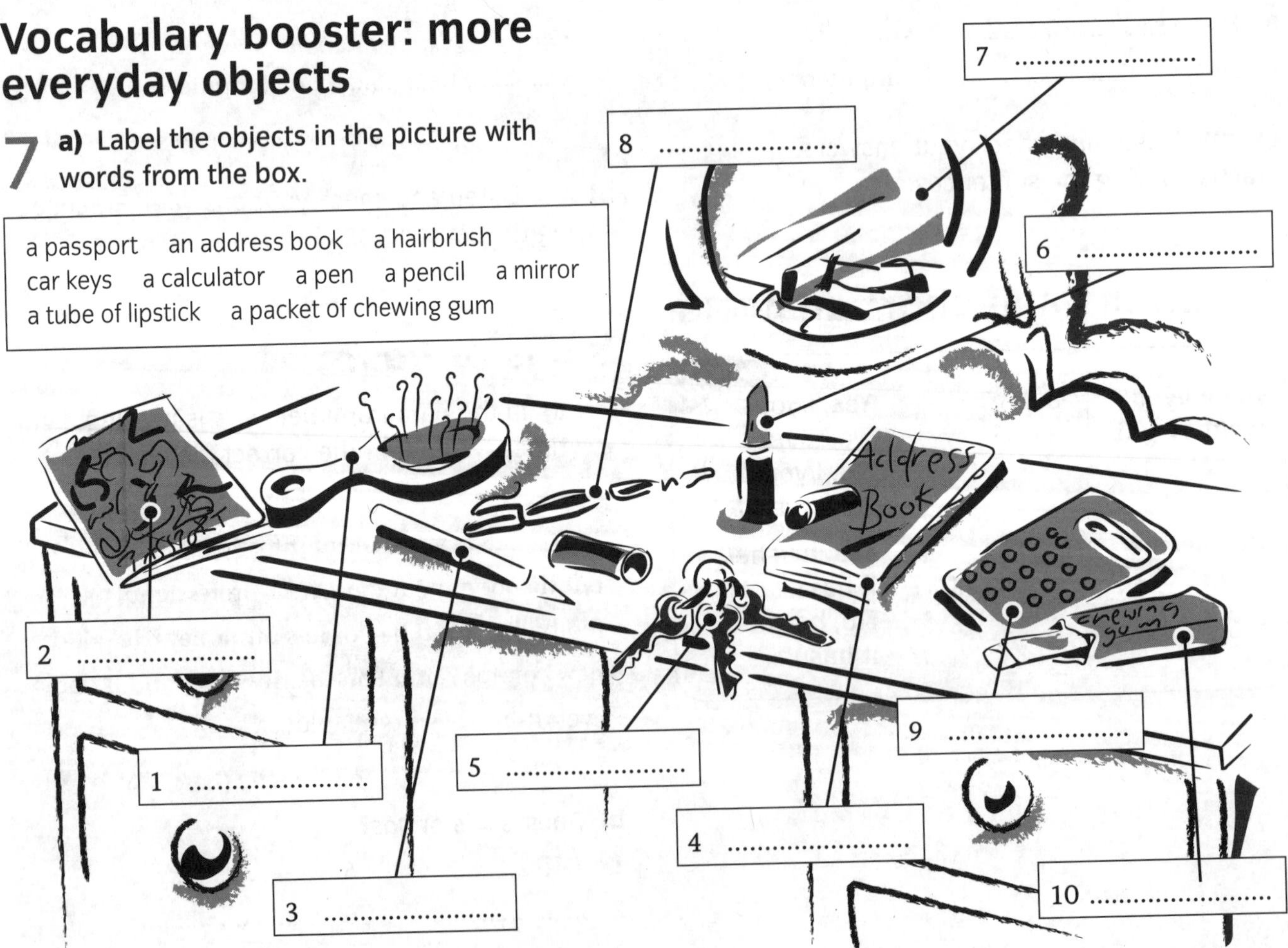

b) Listen to the pronunciation of the words. Practise saying the words.

Vocabulary

Relationship vocabulary

8 **a)** Look at the picture and information about The Doyle Family.

Brenda Doyle – Joe's wife

Joe Doyle – 'Dad'

Jason Doyle – Jane's brother

Colin Best – Jane's husband

Jane Best – Joe and Brenda's daughter

Nora Walker (Nana) – Brenda's mother

The Doyle Family

b) Use the information to complete the sentences.

1 Joe Doyle is Brenda's *husband*.

2 Jason is Joe and Brenda's ....

3 Brenda is Jane and Jason's ....

4 Joe is their ....

5 Joe and Brenda are Jane's ....

6 Colin is Jane's ....

c) Answer the questions with two sentences, as in the example.

1 Who is Nora Walker?

She's Brenda's mother.

She's Jane and Jason's grandmother.

2 Who is Jason?

....

....

3 Who is Joe?

....

....

4 Who is Brenda?

....

....

5 Who is Jane?

....

....

6 Who are Jane and Jason?

....

....

Listen and read

9 **a)** Read and listen to the text about the Iglesias family.

A Famous Family

Julio Iglesias is from Spain. The world's number 1 Spanish singer in the 70s and 80s, with songs like *Begin the Beguine*, he is now the father of a famous family. The three children from his marriage in the 1970s to actress Isabel Preysler – two sons and a daughter – are now all famous too.

His daughter, Chaveli, is a TV presenter in the United States. His sons' names are Julio Junior and Enrique: Julio Junior is a model, actor and singer. His songs are in English and Spanish.

Enrique Iglesias is also a singer. His home is in Miami, Florida. He's got two Porsche cars at home!!

b) Complete the information in the family tree about the Iglesias family.

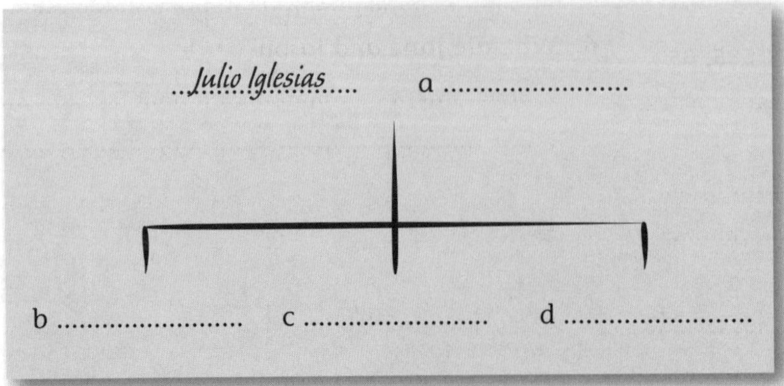

Possessive 's

10 Write 's in the correct place in the sentences, as in the example.

a Patrick is Jane's brother.
b Is that Michael car?
c It's Tessa birthday on Saturday.
d What's your mother name?
e Where's Philip desk?
f My husband name is Peter.
g Jo is my sister friend.
h Carla house is in the centre of Rome.

Spelling

Plurals

11 **a)** Write the plural of these words.

1 diary *diaries*
2 dictionary ……
3 box ……
4 university ……
5 baby ……
6 key ……
7 match ……
8 watch ……
9 house ……
10 bus ……
11 address ……
12 boy ……

b) Rearrange the mixed-up letters to make irregular plurals.

1 h c r n e i l d *children*
2 v s i w e ……
3 e f t e ……
4 n e m ……
5 e n o w m ……
6 s i l e v ……

Pronunciation

The sounds /s/ and /z/

12 **a)** Listen to the pronunciation of the /s/ sound. Underline the /s/ sounds.

What's this?

– It's my passport.

b) Listen to the pronunciation of the /z/ sound. Circle the /z/ sounds.

His friend's name is James.

c) Listen. Underline the /s/ sounds.

1 This is my sister. Her name's Suzanne.
2 Those are my keys!
3 She's seven years old.
4 What's his address?
5 She's got fantastic blue eyes.
6 What's your brother's first name?
7 Sarah is a famous actress.
8 What's the answer to this question?

d) Listen again. Circle the /z/ sounds.

Prepositions

13 Underline the correct preposition.

a What's that *at/in* English?
b Have you got your diary *for/with* you?
c We've got two dogs *at/in* my family.
d John is a student *at/for* Cambridge University.
e We've got cable TV *at/to* home.
f I've got a pen *in/on* my bag.

Improve your writing

Writing about people in your family

14 **a)** Read about the people in this family.

People in my family

My father's name is Martin Hancock. He's 53 years old and he's an architect. He and my mother aren't married now – they're divorced. His new wife's name is Judy. They've got a baby daughter – her name's Cassandra and she's beautiful!!!

My sister, Caroline, is twenty-eight years old, and she's a teacher. She's married. Her husband's name is Marcos – he's from Chile. They've got two daughters: Rebecca, who's five, and Annabel, who's two years old. I'm their aunt!!

My cousin Martha is from Australia. She's nineteen years old, and she isn't married: she's a student at the University of Melbourne. She's got a boyfriend – his name is Mark. He's twenty. He isn't a student: he's a professional musician. The name of his group is MC2.

My grandmother is about 80 years old. Her name is Beatrice. She's got six children – four sons and two daughters – and she's got twenty-three grandchildren!!

b) Write sentences about some people in your family.

e.g.: *My father's name is Karl.*
My sister, Marjana, is twenty years old.

module 3

Present Simple

Questions

1 **a)** Complete the questions with words from the box.

football in Do French like study ~~live~~ you

1 Do you ....*live*.......... in Edinburgh?
2 .... your parents speak English?
3 Do you and your brother like ....?
4 Do .... like Japanese tea, Johnny?
5 Do Sophie and Emily speak ....?
6 Do you all .... economics?
7 Does the White family live .... a flat?
8 Do you .... Indian food, Paula?

b) Listen to the questions on the recording. Practise saying them.

Negatives

2 **a)** Join the two halves to make negative sentences.

1 People in Brazil don't speak — to school.
2 Cats don't like — in the morning.
3 Most people don't go to work — Spanish.
4 Babies don't go — water.
5 Banks in Britain don't close — rock music.
6 Most restaurants don't open — on Sunday.
7 My grandparents don't like — at lunchtime.

b) Listen to the sentences on the recording. Practise saying them.

Positive and negative

3 **a)** Read the information about Thomas and Angela, from Sweden, and Julia and Ken, from Singapore.

Thomas and Angela

Julia and Ken

from	a small town in Sweden	Singapore City
house	5-bedroom house	a small flat in Singapore City
languages	Swedish, English, German	English, Chinese, Malay
likes	classical music, skiing	Chinese food
dislikes	smoking	heavy metal music
drinks	mineral water and coffee	tea and coffee

b) Complete the sentences.

1 Thomas and Angela don't live.......... in a big city.
2 They .... in a big house.
3 They .... English.
4 They .... Chinese.
5 They .... classical music.
6 They .... smoking.
7 They .... mineral water.
8 They .... tea.
9 Julia and Ken live.................... in a big city.
10 They .... in a big house.
11 They .... Chinese and English.
12 They .... German.
13 They .... Chinese food.
14 They .... heavy metal music.
15 They .... milk.
16 They .... tea.

Questions and short answers

4 Answer the questions about Thomas, Angela, Julia and Ken with short answers. Then answer the questions about yourself.

a Do Thomas and Angela live in a small town? Yes, they do.
Do you live in a small town? No, I don't.
b Do they like classical music? ....
Do you like classical music? ....
c Do they speak Chinese? ....
Do you speak Chinese? ....
d Do they drink tea? ....
Do you drink tea? ....
e Do Julia and Ken live in a big city? ....
Do you live in a big city? ....
f Do they speak German? ....
Do you speak German? ....
g Do they like heavy metal music? ....
Do you like heavy metal music? ....
h Do they drink milk? ....
Do you drink milk? ....

Subject and object pronouns

5 LOOK!

I, *you*, *he*, *she*, *it*, *we* and *they* are **subject pronouns.**

me, *you*, *him*, *her*, *it*, *us* and *them* are **object pronouns.**

subject pronoun		object pronoun
I	⇨	me
you	⇨	you
he	⇨	him
she	⇨	her
it	⇨	it
we	⇨	us
they	⇨	them

We use **object pronouns:**

- after prepositions
  *come with **me***
- when the pronoun is the object of the sentence
  *Sarah loves **him***

Correct the pronouns in **bold**, as in the example.

a Is your ice cream OK? Do you like ~~**them**~~ it?
b Is that your sister?
– Yes, it is ... but who's that with **she**?
c We've got a big flat, and my grandparents live with **we**.
d Is that letter for **I**?
e What's her name?
– Karen.
How do you spell **her**?
f Is Peter Martin your boyfriend?
– No!! I don't like **he**!!!
g Do you like the Spice Girls?
– Yes, I do. I love **they**!!
h What's Julia's address?
– I don't know ... I haven't got **him** with **I**.

Vocabulary

Collocations with common verbs

6 Write three words or phrases from the box with each verb below.

in a flat	tea	to school	~~Japanese~~	law	English grammar	~~French~~
mineral water	a snack	home	in a house	~~Spanish~~	milk	a meal
to university	breakfast	economics	in a city			

a speak *French*............ , *Spanish*............ , *Japanese*............
b drink .... , ... , ...
c live .... , ... , ...
d have .... , ... , ...
e go .... , ... , ...
f study .... , ... , ...

Vocabulary booster: buildings

7 **a)** Label the buildings with words from the box.

~~a block of flats~~	a library	a school	a bank	a supermarket
a railway station	a hospital	a hotel		

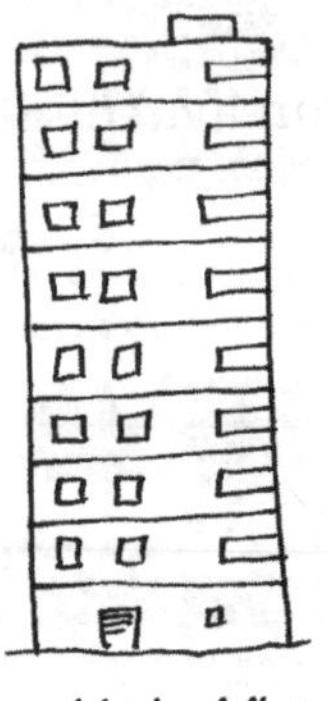

1 *a block of flats*............

2 ....

3 ....

4 ....

5 ....

6 ....

7 ....

8 ....

b) Listen to the pronunciation of the words. Practise saying them.

Listen and read

8 **a)** Read and listen to the text about young people in South Korea.

Studying in South Korea

What time do you have breakfast? Where do you have lunch? Do you go out with your friends for a coffee after school or after work? Do you work in the evenings, or do you have dinner with family or friends?

Life is very different for many young people in South Korea. It's very important for people to go to a good university, and find a good job ... so study is very, very important! Young people get up at about six o'clock, have breakfast with their family, and then go to school ... schools in South Korea start at seven o'clock.

After five hours of lessons in the morning, it's time for lunch. Most people have lunch at school. Then there are more lessons until six o'clock ... but that's not the end! Many young Koreans go to the library and study from about eight o'clock to eleven or twelve o'clock, when the libraries close.

At that time, they go home in a special minibus. Most students don't go to bed before one or two o'clock, and then the next day, after just four or five hours of sleep, it's time to get up again!

b) Answer these questions.

1 What time do most young people get up in South Korea?
They get up at about six o'clock.

2 What time do schools open in South Korea?
....

3 Where do young people have lunch?
....

4 What time do schools in South Korea finish?
....

5 Where do many young people go in the evening?
....

6 What time do the libraries close?
....

7 How do people go home?
....

8 What time do they go to bed?
....

Prepositions: *in*, *at* or *to*

9 Complete the sentences with *in*, *at* or *to*.

a It's 7 o'clock ..*in*.......... the morning.
b He's got a flat .... Essen, a big city .... Germany.
c What time do you go .... bed .... the weekend?
d Is the restaurant open .... the afternoon?
e Do you work .... a bank?
f My brother Frank is .... university.
g Where do you go .... school?
h Do you live .... a big house?
i Most shops close .... lunchtime.
j The shops close .... 10 o'clock .... the evening.

Opposites

10 Rearrange the letters to make opposites.

a finish
 a r t s t ..*start*..........
b morning
 v i n e n e g ....
c go to bed
 t e g p u ....
d open
 s o l c e ....
e go to work
 m o c e m e h o m o r f k r o w
 ....

Pronunciation

The letter *i*

11 **a)** We pronounce the letter *i* in different ways.
Listen to these examples.

/ɪ/ live, city
/aɪ/ I, like

b) Look at the words in the box. Do we pronounce *i* as /ɪ/ or as /aɪ/? Put the words into the correct column.

~~drink~~	six	big	finish	life	this	nine	~~time~~
five	children	write	listen	night	dinner		

/ɪ/	/aɪ/
drink..................	*time*..................
....	....
....	....
....	....
....	....
....	....
....	
....	

c) Listen to the pronunciation of the words. Practise saying them.

Improve your writing

Commas, full stops, *and* and *but*

LOOK!

,	*a comma*
.	*a full stop*
linkers	*and, but*

12 **a)** Write three commas, a full stop and a linker in the sentence below.

In Britain children start school at about 9 o'clock in the morning in Poland they start school at 8 o'clock

b) Use the information in the box to write sentences about the differences between life in New York and life in York, a town in the north of England. Use commas, full stops, *and* or *but*.

	New York, USA	York, UK
Most people live in	flats (= apartments)	houses
Most people start work	8 a.m.	9 a.m.
Most people finish work	6 p.m.	5.30 p.m.
Children start school at	5 years	4 years
Most shops open at	9 a.m.	9 a.m.
Most shops close at	8 p.m.	6 p.m.

1 (New York/live/York/live)
In New York, most people live in apartments, but in York, most people live in houses.

2 (New York/start work/finish work)
In New York, most people start work at 8 a.m., and they finish work at 6 p.m.

3 (New York/start work/York)
....

4 (York/start work/finish work)
....

5 (New York/finish work/York)
....

6 (New York/children start school/York)
....

7 (New York/shops open/close)
....

8 (New York/shops close/York)
....

too, both and *neither*

LOOK!

We use *me too* to agree with a positive sentence.
A: *I love Chinese food.*
B: ***Me too!!***

We use *me neither* to agree with a negative sentence.
A: *I'm not tired.*
B: ***Me neither.***

We use *both* to say that two things or people are the same. Notice the position of *both*.
*We **both** like jazz.*
*They are **both** nineteen years old.*

13 Write *both*, *neither* or *too* in the sentences.

a Are you from the USA?
– Yes, I'm from California.
Oh really? Me *too*..........!

b Paula and her sister are .... teachers.

c I don't like jazz.
– Me ....

d We're here on holiday. How about you?
– Yes, me ....

e I don't understand this film.
– Me ....

f Nick and I .... work at *The Bridge Hotel*.

g I don't take milk in my coffee.
– No, me ....

h Stefan loves basketball.
– Me ....!

module 4

Present Simple

Spelling

1 Write the letters to make the *he/she/it* form.

a My mother read*s* *Hi!* magazine.
b James watch_ _ TV in the morning.
c Winnie come_ from South Korea.
d Richard live_ in the United States.
e She go_ _ to bed at 11 o'clock.
f Francis enjoy_ watching football on TV.
g My brother say_ he's fine.
h Norma stud_ _ _ economics at the University of Leeds.
i Ian always play_ football on Saturday.

Present Simple with *he/she/it*

2 **a)** Look at the information in the chart and complete these sentences about Akiko Murata.

1 She *comes*............... from Japan. (*come*)
2 She .... fashion design. (*study*)
3 She .... in San Francisco. (*live*)
4 She .... Japanese and English. (*speak*)
5 She .... cooking and ballet. (*like*)

	Nationality	Job	Address	Languages	Hobbies
Akiko Murata	Japanese	fashion design student	Golden Gate Ave. San Francisco, USA	Japanese, English	cooking, ballet
David Jones	British	English teacher	The English School, Seoul, South Korea	English, French, Korean	watching football, playing the guitar
Beatriz Ayala	Argentinian	bank employee	Carrer Bonavista Barcelona, Spain	Spanish, Catalan, English	painting, going to the gym
Zoltan Tarnai	Hungarian	music teacher	Rue d'Alleray, Paris, France	Hungarian, French, German	playing tennis, walking

b) Listen to the sentences. Practise saying them.

c) Write sentences about David, Beatriz and Zoltan using the Present Simple.

1 *David Jones teaches English.*.............. (*teach*)
2 He .... (*come from*)
3 .... (*live*)
4 .... (*speak*)
5 .... (*play*)
6 *Beatriz Ayala lives in Spain.*.............. (*live*)
7 She .... (*come from*)
8 .... (*speak*)
9 .... (*work*)
10 .... (*go to the gym*)
11 *Zoltan Tarnai speaks Hungarian, French and German.*.............. (*speak*)
12 He .... (*come from*)
13 .... (*live*)
14 .... (*teach*)
15 .... (*play*)

Short answers

3 **a)** Look at the information about Akiko and David on page 22 and write the correct short answer.

1 Does Akiko come from Japan? *Yes, she does.*
2 Does she study economics? *No, she doesn't.*
3 Does she live in New York? ....
4 Does she speak English? ....
5 Does she like ballet? ....
6 Does David come from the USA? ....
7 Does he teach English? ....
8 Does he live in South Korea? ....
9 Does he speak Chinese? ....
10 Does he play tennis? ....

b) Listen to the questions and answers on the recording. Practise saying them.

Negatives

4 **a)** Make these sentences negative.

1 Maria likes studying grammar.
Maria doesn't like studying grammar.
2 It rains in summer.
....
3 My brother likes getting up at seven o'clock.
....
4 The restaurant closes on Sunday evening.
....
5 Martin comes to class every week.
....
6 Tony buys all his food at the supermarket.
....
7 Carla drives to work.
....
8 My cousin visits me every month.
....

b) Listen to the sentences. Practise saying them.

Positives and negatives

5 Put the verb into the correct form of the Present Simple.

Malcolm Tracey (a) *doesn't go* (*not/go*) to work: he only (b) .... (*leave*) his home town to go on holiday in the Caribbean with his family. But Malcolm is a millionaire. He (c) .... (*write*) books about money, and how to make a lot of it. His new book is called *Easy Money: How to make money without getting out of bed.* Malcolm (d) .... (*live*) in a large house in Bray, a town about 40 kilometres from London. He (e) .... (*get up*) at about 9 o'clock in the morning, and (f) .... (*have*) breakfast with his family. After breakfast, he (g) .... (*drive*) his children to school in his white Rolls Royce, and (h) .... (*read*) the newspaper in his garden until lunchtime. After lunch, he (i) .... (*buy*) and (j) .... (*sell*) on the Internet. He (k) .... (*finish*) work at 4 o'clock when his children come home. 'I've got a simple system for making money,' Malcolm (l) .... (*say*). 'It (m) .... (*not work*) for everybody ... but it (n) .... (*work*) for me!!

Questions

6 Write questions about Malcolm Tracey.

a (Where/live) *Where does he live?*
In Bray.
b (When/get up) ....
At 9 o'clock in the morning.
c (What/do/after breakfast) ....
He drives his children to school.
d (Where/read the newspaper) ....
In the garden.
e (Where/go on holiday) ....
To the Caribbean.
f (What/do after lunch) ....
He buys and sells on the Internet.
g (What time/finish work) ....
At 4 o'clock.

Adverbs of frequency

7 Underline the true sentence.

a In the morning, the sun *always/never/sometimes* comes up in the east.
b Sharks *never/sometimes/often* kill people.
c Children *never/don't often/usually* like sweets.
d In the game of chess, black *always/never/usually* starts.
e People with brown hair *don't often/never/often* have brown eyes.
f Monday *always/often/usually* comes before Tuesday.
g A year *always/never/usually* has 364 days.
h Spiders *always/often/sometimes* have eight legs.

Activity verbs

8 Complete the sentences with verbs from the box.

~~read~~ write watch listen plays go visit study write read go listen

a Do you *read* the newspaper every day?
– No, I don't. I only *read* magazines.
b Do you ever .... swimming at the weekend?
– No, I don't, but I often .... shopping!
c My mother and father always .... a video on a Friday night.
d I usually .... to a CD when I drive to work. I never .... to the radio.
e My brother Hector loves sport: he .... rugby, basketball, tennis and chess!!
f I never .... letters: but I .... a lot of e-mails!!
g I always .... my friend Roger when I'm in London.
h I'm at Edinburgh University.
– What do you ....?
Law.

Word order: frequency adverbs, auxiliaries

9 Put the words in brackets in the correct places in the sentences, as in the example.

a I sometimes have dinner at my friend's house. (*sometimes*)
b Caroline eats fish. (*never*)
c I often eat in a restaurant. (*don't*)
d I get up late on a Sunday morning. (*usually*)
e It's very hot in August in my city. (*always*)
f The Brown family usually to Italy on holiday. (*go*)
g The weather always cold in January. (*is*)
h The bus is late. (*often*)

Vocabulary booster: everyday activities

10 a) Match the phrases from the box with the pictures below.

clean your teeth	have a shower	go for a walk ....
get dressed	wake up	go for a run a........
catch a bus	go to the gym	cook a meal ....
meet friends		

b) Listen to the phrases on the recording. Practise saying them.

c) When do people usually do these things? Make a list.

in the morning	in the afternoon/evening
clean your teeth	clean your teeth
....	....
....	....
....	....
....	....
....	....

like, love, hate + -ing

11 **a)** Read about Irene and Agnes and find out what they like and dislike about their life.

Irene and Agnes are both au pairs: they live with a family, do housework (clean the house) and help with the children. In the afternoon, they go to an English class.
In the evenings they often babysit (they stay at home with the children when their parents go out).

1 = horrible!!! I hate it! *2 = don't like it*
3 = OK *4 = I like it* *5 = fantastic!!! I love it!!*

	Irene	Agnes
taking the children to school	2	4
doing housework	1	5
talking to the family	5	2
going to English class	4	1
babysitting	2	4

b) Write about their likes and dislikes.

1 (*taking the children to school*)
Irene doesn't like taking the children to school.
Agnes likes taking the children to school.

2 (*doing housework*)
Irene ....
Agnes ....

3 (*talking to the family*)
Irene ....
Agnes ....

4 (*going to English class*)
Irene ....
Agnes ....

5 (*babysitting*)
Irene ....
Agnes ....

Listen and read

12 **a)** Read and listen to the text about English people's homes abroad.

'An Englishman's home,' they say, 'is his castle.' Perhaps that's true ... but nowadays the home often isn't in England ... it's abroad!

More than half a million British people have a second home in another country. Many buy old houses in the south of France, or in Tuscany, in the north of Italy. The Eurostar train, which goes from London to Paris in three hours, makes it easy to go from one home to the other quickly. The Noteman family, who live in London, have got a small house in Gascony. They sometimes go there for weekends, and they always spend the summer in France with their four children. Jerry Noteman says, 'We really like living in France: the weather is usually good, we like the food and the wine and the people are very friendly. We don't usually speak French when we go out ... most of our neighbours in the village are English, too!.'

b) Answer these questions:

1 How many British people have a home abroad?
More than half a million.

2 Where do they often buy houses?
....

3 Where does the Eurostar train go to?
....

4 Where do the Noteman family live in England?
....

5 Where do they live in France?
....

6 Where do they spend the summer?
....

7 How many children do they have?
....

8 What do they like about living in France?
....

9 Where do most of their neighbours come from?
....

Pronunciation

Plural nouns with /s/, /z/ and /ɪz/.

13 **a)** Listen and notice the pronunciation of the plural form of these words.

shop	shops	/s/
key	keys	/z/
bus	buses	/ɪz/

b) Write the plural form of the nouns below. Do we pronounce the *s* at the end of the word as /s/, /z/ or /ɪz/?

1 dogs ../z/..
2 crowd_ ....
3 spider_ ....
4 actress_ ....
5 beach_ ....
6 driver_ ....
7 student_ ....
8 restaurant_ ....
9 house_ ....
10 friend_ ....
11 parent_ ....
12 address_ ....

c) Listen to the pronunciation of the words. Practise saying them.

Improve your writing

A paragraph about a friend

14 **a)** Match the questions and answers.

1 What's his name? ...C...
2 Where does he come from? ....
3 Where does he live now? ....
4 What does he do? ....
5 Where does he play? ....
6 What does he like about life in London? ....
7 What does he dislike about life in London? ....
8 What does he think of the people? ....

A He's a musician.
B In a bar called *East and West.*
C ~~Takashi~~.
D They're very nice when you know them.
E The rain.
F In London.
G Okinawa, in Japan.
H The international atmosphere.

b) Use the information to write a paragraph about Takashi, like this:

My friend Takashi .... Okinawa, in Japan, but now he .... in London. .... a musician, and .... in a bar called *East and West.* He .... the international atmosphere in London, but .... the rain! He .... the people are very nice ....

module 5

can/can't

1 Look at the motorway signs. What can/can't you do on the motorway? Complete the sentences.

a You ....*can't*.... stop on the motorway.

b You .... drive at 100 kilometres an hour.

c You .... drive at 180 kilometres an hour.

d You .... ride a bicycle on the motorway.

e You .... walk on the motorway.

f You .... find something to eat and drink at the service station.

g You .... buy petrol at the service station.

h You .... turn round.

i Learner drivers .... use the motorway.

Short answers

2

> **Short answers with *can***
>
> **Can** I/you/he/she/we/they drive? — Yes, I/you/he/she/we/they **can**. No, I/you/he/she/we/they **can't**.
>
> LOOK!

a) Write the short answers.

NO PARKING
MONDAY - SATURDAY 9.30 - 5.30

1 It's 8.30 in the morning. Can I park here? ....

2 Can I park here on a Sunday? ....

3 Can I smoke here? ....

SMOKING AREA

4 Can I smoke here? ....

SORRY No children under 18

5 Tom and Barbara are 16 years old. Can they go in? ....

6 I'm 19 years old. Can I go in? ....

7 Can I cross the road now? ....

8 I've got a dog. Can it come in? ....

9 Excuse me, can we buy a phonecard here? ....

b) Listen to the questions and answers. Practise saying them.

Articles: *a* and *the*

3 Write *a* or *the* in the correct places in the sentences, as in the examples.

a Can you ride a bicycle?

b Does it take a long time to get to the centre of London?

c I always drive to work, but lot of people come by underground.

d Parking is real problem near my house.

e The traffic is very bad in evening.

f My uncle is train driver.

g Have you got car?

h We live in small town in United States.

4 In each sentence, one *the* is unnecessary. Cross it out, as in the example.

a Parking is very difficult in the city centre, so I always go there by ~~the~~ bus.

b 8 o'clock is a good time to phone Thomas: he is always at the home in the evening.

c It's so cold today that a lot of people can't go to the work.

d The train times are different on the Sundays.

e What do you think of the public transport in the London?

f You can use a Rail Card in most countries in the Europe.

g Do the people drive on the left in the United States?

h Our plane arrives in Los Angeles at the 2 o'clock in the afternoon.

most, a lot of, some, not many

5 Rearrange the words to make sentences.

a a bicycle – children – learn – Most – to ride

Most children learn to ride a bicycle.

b many – Not – on – people – Sundays – work

....

c on holiday – British people – A lot of – go to Spain

....

d can't – coffee – drink – without sugar – people – Some

....

e lot of – flying – like – people – A – don't

....

f Not many – understand – Japanese – European people – can

....

g enjoy – to tourists – Most – in my town – people – talking

....

h drive – night – at – Some – people – dangerously

....

Listen and read

6 **a)** Listen to and read the text about transport statistics.

Transport Statistics

6 is the number of hours it takes to travel from London to New York by plane.

44 is the number of platforms at New York's Grand Central Terminal Station. Half a million people use the station every day.

209 kilometres an hour is the speed of the Spanish AVE train, which goes from the capital city Madrid to Seville, in the south of Spain, a distance of 470 km. The journey takes about two and a half hours.

567 is the number of passengers who can travel in a Boeing 747-400 aeroplane. It can fly for more than 12,000 kilometres without stopping. That's from London to Tokyo and back again.

9,297 kilometres is the distance of the Trans-Siberian railway, which goes from Moscow to the town of Vladivostok in eastern Russia. The journey takes seven days.

60,000 is the number of taxis in Mexico City.

6,000,000 is the total kilometres of roads in the United States.

43,000,000 is the number of people who travel through Heathrow Airport, near London, every year.

b) Answer the questions about the text.

1 How long does it take to travel from Madrid to Seville by the *AVE* train?
Two and a half hours.

2 Where does the Trans-Siberian railway begin?
....

3 How many people can travel on a Boeing 747-400 aeroplane?
....

4 Which country has 6,000,000 kilometres of road?
....

5 How many people pass through Heathrow Airport every year?
....

6 Which city has 60,000 taxis?
....

7 Which railway station has 44 platforms?
....

8 How long does it take to fly from London to New York?
....

Prepositions

7 Complete the sentences with *by*, *to*, *on*, *off*, *for* or *from*.

a Most people go to work ...*by*....................... car.

b It's not possible to drive to the beach: go .... foot.

c My journey .... work usually takes about 30 minutes.

d In Thailand, cars drive .... the left.

e You can fly .... Scotland direct from Paris.

f This is where you wait .... a bus to the railway station.

g Please wait for people to get .... the bus before you get ....

h I never walk .... town: I always go .... bus.

i This bus goes .... the airport to the city centre.

j It's a good idea to walk .... work in the morning.

Vocabulary

Means of transport

8 What are the missing letters?

a B*U*S

b M _ T _ R B _ K _

c S C _ _ T _ R

d B _ C _ C L _

e C _ R

f _ _ R _ P L _ N _

g T R _ M

h T R _ _ N

i _ N D _ R G R _ _ N D

j T _ X _

Vocabulary booster: travel

9 a) Match the words from the box with the pictures.

traffic lights	a bus stop	a platform ...1...
a pedestrian crossing	a motorway	
a ticket machine	a railway bridge	a car park ....
a pavement	a parking meter	

b) Listen to the words. Practise saying them.

Pronunciation

The letter *a*

10 a) We can pronounce the letter *a* in different ways.

/aː/	/eɪ/	/ɔː/	/æ/
artist	make	walk	catch
..can't..	....	....	....
....	....	....	....
....	....	....	....

b) Write these words in the correct column above.

~~can't~~	taxi	take	small
train	far	talk	traffic jam
car	travel	wait	football

c) Listen to the words. Practise saying them.

Spelling

11 Find **ten** spelling mistakes. Underline and correct them, as in the example.

Everybody knows that the traffic <u>trafic</u> in our city is really bad, and there are always traffic jams in the morning and evning. I haven't got a car, so like most people, I usually travell by bus. My jorney home takes more than an hour. Also, the bus is very croded and sometimes I have to wait a long time for a bus wich isn't full.

If I rid my bicicle, it only takes therty minutes ... but it isn't easy because of all the cars on the rode.

Improve your writing

Completing an immigration form

12 Use the information below and complete Robert's immigration form.

YOUR FLIGHT DETAILS

For:	PRESTON / R MR
Booking Ref:	GSKTFM
Date of Flight:	THURSDAY, OCTOBER 15, 01
From:	LIMA
To:	MIAMI
Airline:	AMERICAN AIRWAYS
Flight no:	AA 9295

PASSPORT

UNITED KINGDOM OF GREAT BRITAIN AND NORTHE

Name of bearer
Mr. Robert Alexander PRESTON

National Status
UK CITIZEN

No. of passport
737935 G

Place of Birth
Eastbourne, East Sussex

Date of Birth
12 February 1981

P<GBRPRESTON<<ROBERT<ALEXANDER<<
00050749066GBR810212M080212<<<<<<<<<<<

VISA WAIVER Immigration

Type or print legibly with pen in ALL CAPITAL LETTERS. **USE ENGLISH**.

1. Family name
2. First (given) name
3. Birth Date (*day / mo / yr*)
4. Country of Citizenship
5. Sex (*male or female*)
6. Passport Number
7. Airline and Flight Number
8. Country where you live
9. City where you boarded

CERTIFICATION: I certify that I have read and understand all the questions and statements on this form. The answers I have furnished are true and correct to the best of my knowledge and belief.

Signature ______________ Date ______________

module 6

Countable and uncountable nouns

1 a) Nine more of the words in the box are uncountable nouns. Circle them.

butter fruit meat water tea journey cheese hamburger egg vegetable music bread food sugar knife biscuit

b) Underline the correct word or words, as in the example.

1 Check that the water *are/is* clean before you drink it.
2 The sugar *is/are* on the table.
3 The food in our hotel *aren't/isn't* very good. We eat all our *meal/meals* in a restaurant.
4 The journey from Miami to London *take/takes* about six hours.
5 Do you like *these/this* music? *It's/They're* by Mozart.
6 Everybody says that vegetables *are/is* very good for you.
7 It's not healthy to eat *too much/too many* hamburgers.
8 Fruit *isn't/aren't* expensive in my country.

Vocabulary

Food

2 In the box, find:

Drinks	**Types of fruit**	**Other things you can eat**	
mineral water......	*banana*......	......	......
......	......	......	......
......	......	......	......
......	......	......	......
......		......	......
		......	......

J	O	J	A	M	H	A	N	N	S	C	E
B	F	A	S	B	U	T	T	E	R	O	T
B	R	E	A	D	I	E	A	O	N	F	B
N	U	T	S	G	B	A	A	R	C	F	H
M	I	N	E	R	A	L	W	A	T	E	R
P	T	A	A	A	N	P	I	N	R	E	Y
T	J	P	I	P	A	I	C	G	C	T	O
A	U	P	N	E	N	Z	E	E	H	U	G
M	I	L	K	S	A	Z	M	M	E	E	H
R	C	E	G	G	S	A	E	H	E	I	U
C	E	R	E	A	L	T	O	A	S	T	R
S	A	U	S	A	G	E	S	M	E	N	T

there is/there are

3 Complete the sentences with the correct form of *there is/there are*.

a *Is there*........ any milk in the fridge?
b How many students .... in your class?
c .... a very good beach near our hotel.
d .... any cheap restaurants near here?
e .... a university in Brighton?
f I'm sorry, but .... any shops open at this time.
g .... fifty states in the USA.
h .... any milk: how about lemon in your tea?
i .... a computer room in the school?
j .... three big parks in the city.

Short answers

4 **a)** Read the information about two campsites: *Les Pins* and *Las Molinas*.

Les Pins	Las Molinas
Five minutes' walk to the beach	Beautiful mountain location
Tennis courts	Swimming pool
Restaurant, drinks bar	Bar
Children's playground	Supermarket, souvenir shop
Shops etc. in village of Choisy (5 km)	10 km from the historic town of Los Pozos (shops, restaurants, pubs etc.)

LOOK!

Short answers with *there is* and *there are*

Is there a hotel near here?	Yes, **there is**. No, **there isn't**.
Are there any good restaurants?	Yes, **there are**. No, **there aren't**.

b) Complete the questions, and write the correct short answer.

at *Les Pins*:

1 *Is*........... there a beach?
Yes, there is.
2 .... there any places to eat and drink?
....
3 .... there a swimming pool?
....
4 .... there a children's playground?
....
5 .... there a supermarket?
....

at *Las Molinas:*

6 .... there a beach?
No, there isn't.
7 .... there a restaurant?
....
8 .... there any tennis courts?
....
9 .... a bar?
....
10 .... there any shops?
....
11 .... there any interesting towns to visit?
....

c) Listen to the sentences on the recording. Practise saying them.

some and *any*

5 a) Complete the sentences with *some* or *any*.

1 No, thanks, I don't drink coffee ... have got you got ..*any*........ orange juice?
2 There are .... messages for you on the answering machine.
3 There's .... salt on the table, but there isn't .... pepper.
4 We can't make an omelette because we haven't got .... eggs.
5 Would you like .... milk in your coffee?
6 There's .... butter on the table.
7 Sorry, we haven't got .... more bread. Would you like .... biscuits with your cheese?
8 I'm sorry, we haven't got .... hot food, but we've got .... sandwiches if you're hungry.

b) Listen to the sentences on the recording. Practise saying them.

some, *any*, *a(n)* and *no*

6 a) Helen and Carlos want to buy a sandwich for their lunch. Complete the conversation in the sandwich shop with *some*, *any*, *a(n)* or *no*.

ASSISTANT: Yes, what would you like?
HELEN: Let me see ... I'd like (1) ..*an*......... egg sandwich, please.
ASSISTANT: OK, one egg sandwich ... butter?
HELEN: No, thanks, (2) .... butter. I'm on (3) .... diet.
ASSISTANT: OK ... here you are. Anything else with that? We've got (4) .... very nice fruit ... bananas, apples ...
HELEN: Yes. (5) .... apple, please.
ASSISTANT: OK, that's £2.50. And for you, sir?
CARLOS: Hmm. Have you got (6) .... Swiss cheese?
ASSISTANT: No, sorry. There's (7) .... Swiss cheese, but we've got (8) .... very good Cheddar ... it's English cheese, it's very good.
CARLOS: OK. (9) .... Cheddar cheese sandwich, please. Can I have (10) .... salad with that?
ASSISTANT: Sure. Would you like (11) .... drink?
HELEN: Yes, (12) .... bottle of mineral water, please.

b) Listen to the conversation. Practise saying it.

Vocabulary booster: things to eat

7 **a)** Label the pictures with words from the box.

~~rice~~ crisps potatoes salt salad oil olives tomatoes pepper onions French fries vinegar

1 *rice* .... 7 ....

2 .... 8 ....

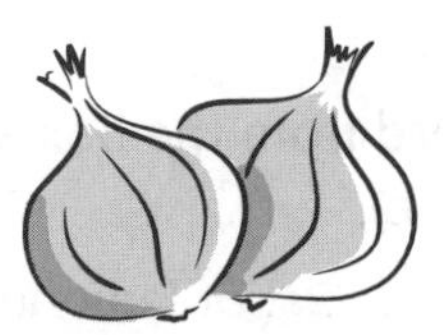

3 .... 9 ....

4 .... 10 ....

5 .... 11 ....

6 .... 12 ....

b) Listen to the pronunciation of the words.

Listen and read

8 Read and listen to the recipe. Tick (✓) the correct picture.

Ⓐ

Ⓑ

Ⓒ

Ⓓ

Fish Cakes

Ingredients (to make 24 fish cakes):

500g boiled potatoes
350g cooked white fish
1 tablespoon tomato purée
2 tablespoons mixed herbs
50g breadcrumbs
a little oil
salt and pepper

Method:

1 Mash the boiled potatoes with a little salt and pepper.
2 Mix together the potatoes and the fish, tomato purée and herbs.
3 Add a little salt and pepper.
4 Make 24 fish cakes from the mixture. Cover the fish cakes with the breadcrumbs.
5 Heat the oil in a frying pan. Fry the fish cakes for about five minutes, turning them once.
6 Serve the fish cakes immediately with tomato sauce and a salad.

Questions with *how much* and *how many*

9 Complete these questions about the recipe on page 37, using *how much* or *how many*.

a *How many*........ fish cakes does this recipe make?
– Twenty-four.

b .... fish do you need?
– 350g.

c .... potato do you use in the recipe?
– 500g.

d .... tablespoons of herbs do you need?
– Two.

e .... tomato purée do you add?
– 1 tablespoon.

f .... oil do you use?
– A little.

g .... grams of breadcrumbs do you need?
– 50.

h .... minutes do you cook the fishcakes?
– About five.

Vocabulary

Containers: *a cup of, a glass of, a bottle of*

10 **a)** Label the pictures with words from the box.

a bag	a bottle	a carton	~~a cup~~	a glass	a packet

1 *a cup*........
2 ....
3 ....
4 ....
5 ....
6 ....

b) Complete the phrases with a suitable word from the box above (sometimes more than one answer is possible).

1 a *bottle*...... of mineral water
2 a .... of cigarettes
3 a .... of milk
4 a .... of sugar
5 a .... of biscuits
6 a .... of lemonade
7 a .... of coffee
8 a .... of water
9 a .... of orange juice
10 a .... of tea

Pronunciation

Sentence stress

11 **a)** Listen to the recording. Underline the words which have the main sentence stress, as in the example.

1 Can I have a bottle of mineral water, please?
2 You can catch a bus to the airport from here.
3 How many packets of cigarettes do you buy in a week?
4 How much money have you got in your bag?
5 I always have orange juice with my breakfast.
6 How much water do you drink in a day?
7 What do you want for lunch?
8 I never drink coffee in the evening.

b) Listen again and practise saying the sentences.

Improve your writing

Describing food from your country

12 **a)** What nationality is the writer of each paragraph? Choose from the words in the box.

Italian	Mexican	Argentinian	Japanese	French	Hungarian	Spanish

1 .... 2 .... 3 .... 4 .... 5 ....

①
Pizza is a very famous food from my country. Originally it comes from Naples, in the south of my country. A traditional pizza has cheese – mozzarella cheese – tomato and herbs. A lot of young people go to a pizza restaurant on Sunday evenings.
Andrea

②
People don't use a knife and fork to eat the traditional food of my country: we use wooden sticks called chopsticks. Sushi is a very famous dish with fish, rice and sometimes vegetables.
Kaori

③
A typical breakfast in my country is a very big cup of strong coffee, with lots of milk. The traditional thing to eat with your coffee is a croissant, maybe with butter or jam.
Jean-Christophe

④
People eat a lot of meat in my country, especially beef. On Sundays, people have a traditional lunch called an asado. In my family, my father cooks the meat on a barbecue, and we eat it with lots of salad
Oscar

⑤
The national dish of my country is gulyásleves. Many people think it's a meat dish but if you have real gulyás, it's a soup with lots of meat and vegetables.
Eva

b) Write a few sentences about food in your country. Use some of these phrases to help you.

Useful Language

… is a very famous food from my country.
Originally it comes from … in the south/north of my country.
The national dish of my country is … .
… is a famous dish with … and … .
A typical breakfast in my country is … .
The traditional thing to eat with … is … .
People eat a lot of … in my country.
On Sunday, many people have … for lunch.
We eat it with lots of … .

module 7

Past Simple: *was/were*

1 Complete the sentences with *was* or *were*.

a My grandparents ....*were*.... married for more than fifty years.
b When I .... in Berlin last year, the weather .... very cold.
c How many people .... there at the party?
d 'Where .... you on Saturday evening?'
e It .... a beautiful day in August. My family and I .... on holiday at the seaside.
f .... George at school today?
g 'How .... your first day at work?'
h It .... very nice to meet you, Mr Brown.

Short answers

LOOK!

Short answers with *was* and *were*

Question	Short answer
Was I/he/she/it OK?	Yes, I/he/she/it **was**. No, he/she/it **wasn't**.
Were you/we/they OK?	Yes, you/we/they **were**. No, you/we/they **weren't**.

2 **a)** Read about the famous people. Complete the questions and the short answers.

Mark Twain
American writer – born 1835 – died 1910

1 ..*Was*....... Mark Twain a painter?
No, he wasn't....
2 ..*Was*....... he American?
Yes, he was....

Charlie Chaplin
Film actor – born London 1889 – died Switzerland 1977

3 .... Charlie Chaplin born in America?
....
4 .... he an actor?
....

The Marx Brothers
American comedians – all born in Germany

5 .... the Marx Brothers born in the USA?
....
6 .... they comedians?
....

Anna Pavlova
Russian dancer – died 1931

7 .... Anna Pavlova Russian?
....
8 .... she a singer?
....

b) Listen to the recording. Practise saying the questions and answers.

Past Simple

Spelling of -*ed* endings.

3 Write the Past Simple tense of the verbs below.

a like *liked*.........
b enjoy ....
c travel ....
d study ....
e look ....
f dance ....
g play ....
h believe ....
i arrive ....
j try ....
k receive ....
l stay ....

Regular verbs

4 Complete the sentences in the Past Simple. Use a verb from the box below.

~~graduate~~ study change try start die end live help walk

a My brother was at Glasgow University: he *graduated*.... last year.
b The Second World War .... in 1939, and .... six years later, in 1945.
c Elvis Presley – The King of Rock'n'Roll – .... in 1977.
d There were no more buses, so I .... home.
e When I was at school, my parents often .... me with my homework.
f I .... French when I was at school, but I don't remember very much now.
g I .... to phone you last night, but there was no answer.
h When he was a young musician, Reg Dwight .... his name to Elton John.
i The composer Chopin was born in Poland, but he .... in France for many years.

Irregular verbs

5 Complete the sentences with the past forms of the verbs in brackets.

Three Child Stars of the Past

Mozart ...

a *wrote*.......... music when he was five years old; (*write*)
b .... home when he was only twelve years old; (*leave*)
c .... to live in Vienna when he was 25 years old. (*go*)

Wolfgang Amadeus Mozart – composer

Donny Osmond ...

d .... singing on television at the age of five; (*begin*)
e .... with his five brothers in the Osmond Brothers; (*sing*)
f .... millions of records before he was 18. (*sell*)

Donny Osmond – pop star

Shirley Temple ...

g .... her first film when she was six; (*make*)
h .... an Oscar in 1934; (*win*)
i .... a politician in the 1970s. (*become*)

Shirley Temple – actress

Regular and irregular verbs

6 **a)** Complete this text about Amelia Earhart, using the correct form of the verbs.

Seventy years ago, Amelia Earhart (1) *was* (be) America's favourite woman. In 1932, she (2) .... (*fly*) across the Atlantic Ocean alone: the first woman to do this. Her journey (3) .... (*start*) in Newfoundland, Canada: fifteen hours later, her Lockheed Vega airplane (4) .... (*arrive*) in Londonderry, Ireland. People all over the world (5) .... (*want*) to meet this incredible woman. She (6) .... (*meet*) King George V of England and (7) .... (*become*) friends with the US President, Franklin D. Roosevelt. The American people (8) .... (*love*) her.

Five years later, Amelia (9) .... (*try*) to fly around the world. An American University (10) .... (*give*) her $50,000 for a new Lockheed Electra airplane. On the morning of July 2nd 1937, Amelia and her co-pilot, Fred Noonan (11) .... (*leave*) Lae, in New Guinea, and (12) .... (*begin*) their journey to Howland Island in the Pacific Ocean.

On July 3rd 1937, the American ship *Itasca* (13) .... (*receive*) a radio message from Amelia: a few minutes later her plane (14) .... (*disappear*). American ships (15) .... (*spend*) nearly two weeks looking for the plane, but they (16) .... (*find*) nothing.

b) Listen and check your answers.

Past time phrases

7 Underline the correct time phrase to complete each sentence.

a Disco music was very popular *nowadays*/*in the 1970s*.

b People started travelling by train *in the 19th century*/*in the 21st century*.

c People usually go to university *when they are 18*/*when they were 18*.

d My family lived in the United States *now*/*when I was a child*.

e Yugoslavia were world basketball champions *in 1990*/*now*.

f I go to the swimming pool *every week*/*last week*.

g I visited my friends in Canada *three years ago*/*every year*.

Prepositions of time

8 Complete the sentences with *at*, *from*, *in*, *on* or *to*.

a The economic situation in our country became much better ..*in*........ the 1990s.

b The café is open .... 8.30 in the morning .... about 11 o'clock in the evening.

c We arrived at the hotel .... about 11 o'clock.

d We decided to have our holidays .... September, when it's not so hot.

e .... the age of seven, Vanessa started dancing lessons.

f I stayed at home .... Friday because I had so much work to do.

g 'When were you born?'
'............... 1986.'

h There was a war between the two countries .... the nineteenth century.

Pronunciation

Past tense endings

9 **a)** Look at the past forms below. Is the pronunciation of the underlined sounds the same (S) or different (D)?

1	bought	caught	*S*........
2	wrote	cost	*D*........
3	said	read	....
4	put	cut	....
5	saw	found	....
6	came	gave	....
7	lost	cost	....
8	took	stood	....
9	wore	caught	....
10	heard	won	....

b) Listen to the recording. Practise saying the words. Copy the voices.

Vocabulary booster: common verbs

10 **a)** Label the pictures with the words from the box.

~~break~~ build catch cut fall run steal throw wake up win

b) Here are the past forms of the verbs in the box. Write the infinitive form next to the past form.

1	broke	*break*	6	ran	....
2	caught	....	7	stole	....
3	built	....	8	fell	....
4	threw	....	9	cut	....
5	woke up	....	10	won	....

c) Listen to the pronunciation of the infinitive and past forms. Practise saying them, copying the voices on the recording.

Listen and read

11 **a)** Read and listen to the story of *The Strange Soldier*.

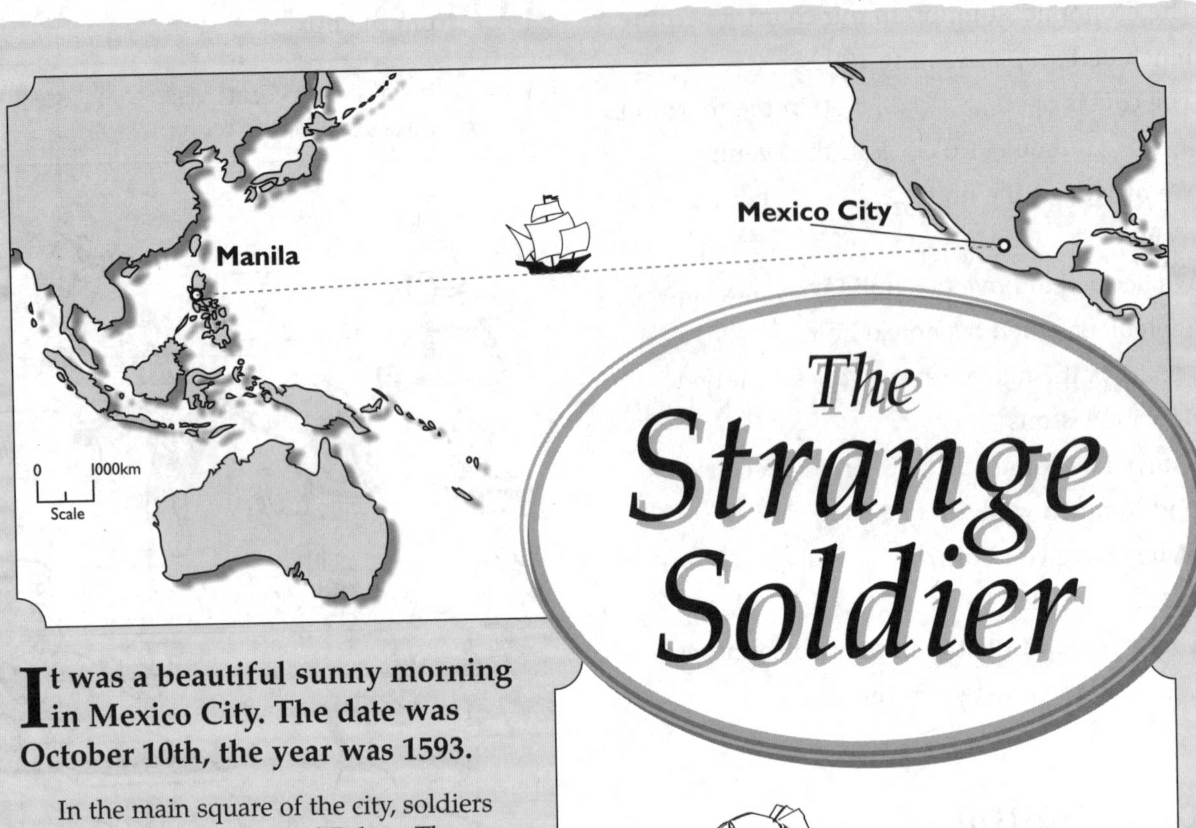

It was a beautiful sunny morning in Mexico City. The date was October 10th, the year was 1593.

In the main square of the city, soldiers stood in front of the Royal Palace. The people of the city came and went as usual. But there was something strange about one of the soldiers: he wore a different uniform from the others, and had a different type of gun. When the other soldiers saw him, they began asking him questions.'Who are you? Where are you from?' one of the other soldiers asked. 'I am a Spanish soldier,' he answered 'and because the governor died last night, it is my job to stay in front of the palace here.' 'The governor?' one of the soldiers replied, 'Which governor?' 'The governor of Manila, of course.'

The other soldiers told him he was in Mexico City – thousands of kilometres from the city of Manila.

The young soldier was amazed and had no idea how he came to be in a city so far from his home. Nobody believed his strange story.

In the end, they put the young man in prison, and left him there until they decided what to do.

Two months later, a Spanish ship arrived from Manila. It brought news that the governor of Manila was dead – and the time of his death was 10 pm on the evening of October 9th, 1593. Was the young man's story true?

400 years later, no one knows how it was possible for a man to travel across the world in one night ... without knowing how or why.

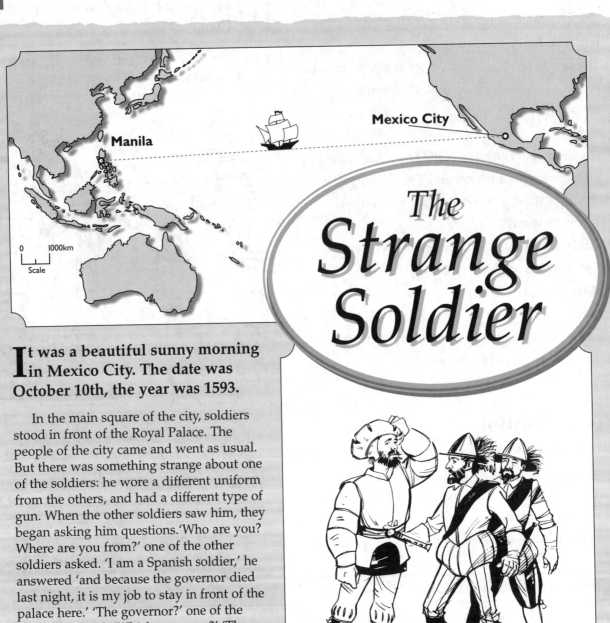

b) Read the story again. Put these events in the order they happened.

A The Mexican soldiers saw the strange soldier. ....
B The governor of Manila died. ....*1*.....
C They put the strange soldier in prison. ....
D A ship from Manila arrived in Mexico City. ....
E The strange soldier travelled from Manila to Mexico. ....

Ordinal numbers

12 Write an ordinal number to complete the sentences. Use the numbers to help you.

a Ronald Reagan was the .*fortieth*........ President of the United States. (*40*)
b 'What's the .... month in the year?' (*5*) 'May.'
c Our apartment is on the .... floor. (*8*)
d Beethoven wrote his music in the .... century. (*19*)
e Brazil won the World Cup for the .... time in 1994. (*4*)
f The Berlin Wall fell near the end of the .... century. (*20*)
g Neil Armstrong was the .... man on the moon, and Buzz Aldrin was the .... (*1/2*)
h My sister's birthday is on the .... of August. (*22*)

Improve your writing

13 Time linkers: *before*, *after*, *then*

LOOK!

Before I went to bed, I phoned Suzanne.
I phoned Suzanne **before** I went to bed.

After Jane left university, she travelled to India.
Jane travelled to India **after** she left university.

Sebastian was a waiter in a restaurant.
Then he found another job.

Join the sentences below with *before*, *after* or *then*.

a .*Before*......... I went home, I bought something to eat from the supermarket.
b .... their dog died, the house was very quiet.
c We had time for a coffee .... the train left.
d In the morning, I went shopping with my friend Sara. .... we had lunch.
e For a long time, nobody spoke. .... someone asked a question.
f .... they got married, Paul and Linda usually stayed at home on Saturday nights.
g .... he was a famous actor, Bruce worked as a taxi driver.
h I remembered to close all the windows .... I went out.

module 8

Vocabulary

Common verbs in the past tense

1 Complete the sentences with the past tense of the verbs in brackets.

a Chris was so hungry he *ate*.............. (*eat*) three burgers and two plates of chips!

b We went shopping on Saturday – I .... (*buy*) a new skirt.

c I .... (*read*) *Alice in Wonderland* when I was seven years old.

d It was a very long journey, but I .... (*sleep*) on the train for a few hours.

e I .... (*see*) my cousin in the park.

f It was a beautiful day on Sunday, so we .... (*drive*) to the country and had a picnic.

g Do you know who .... (*write*) *Don Quijote* ?

h I'm sorry I'm late ... when I .... (*wake up*) it was nearly 10 o'clock!

i Is it true that Robin Hood always .... (*wear*) green?

j The police looked everywhere for the money, but they only .... (*find*) an empty bag.

k Lucy's parents .... (*give*) her a car for her 21st birthday.

l We were so hot and thirsty that we both .... (*drink*) a litre bottle of mineral water.

m It was a very boring concert. Some people .... (*fall*) asleep.

Past Simple

Negative

2 Make the sentences below negative.

a We had good weather when we were on holiday.
We didn't have good weather when we were on holiday.

b We went for a drive yesterday.
....

c Ben remembered to buy a birthday card.
....

d I heard the telephone.
....

e The letter arrived this morning.
....

f I ate in a restaurant last night.
....

g Amanda knew what to do.
....

h I checked my e-mail yesterday.
....

Questions

3 Write questions about these famous people from the past.

a Shakespeare/write/*Romeo and Juliet*
Did Shakespeare write 'Romeo and Juliet'?

b Alexander Graham Bell/invent/e-mail
....

c Marilyn Monroe/sing/*Candle in the Wind*
....

d Captain Cook/discover/America
....

e Leonardo da Vinci/paint/*Mona Lisa*
....

f Madonna/play/*Evita*
....

g Beethoven/write/rock songs

....

h Laurel and Hardy/make/comedy films

....

i Yuri Gagarin/travel/to the moon

....

Short answers

4

> **Short answers with the Past Simple** LOOK!
> **Did** I/you/he/she/it/we/they know?
>
> **Yes**, I/you/he/she/it/we/they **did**.
> **No**, I/you/he/she/it/we/they **didn't**.

a) Look again at the questions in exercise 3. Write the correct short answer for each question.

1 *Yes, he did.* ....
2 ....
3 ....
4 ....
5 ....
6 ....
7 ....
8 ....
9 ....

b) Listen to the questions and answers on the recording. Practise saying them.

Question words

5 **a)** A few days ago, Simon went on a business trip. Look at the papers in his wallet, and write questions about his day.

Eurolink

London - Paris (SINGLE)
Departure time 14.30
Journey time 3 HOURS

The Station Buffet Restaurant
1 set menu £14.50
+ SERVICE (10%)
Total £15.95

The Station Bookshop
Blue Guide to France 9.99
English–French Dictionary 4.99

BUREAU DE CHANGE
£200 changed to French francs

1 *Where did he* .... go?
He went to Paris.

2 .... travel?
By train.

3 .... have lunch?
At *The Station Buffet Restaurant*.

4 .... cost?
£15.95.

5 .... at the station?
Some books.

6 .... buy?
Two.

7 .... change?
£200.

8 .... leave?
At 14.30.

9 .... take?
Three hours.

b) Listen to the questions and answers on the recording. Practise saying them.

Past Simple

Positive, negative and question forms

6 Underline the word that is **incorrect** in the following sentences. Write in the correct word.

a Did you had have a nice weekend?
b Did you see Jan at the party? – Yes, I saw.
c I'm sorry, what did you said?
d What time did you got up this morning?
e It was a very long flight: the journey take more than thirteen hours.
f We went to the shopping centre yesterday, but we didn't bought anything.
g I come home early because I felt very tired.
h Did you enjoyed the film?
i I didn't understood what they said to me.
j Where did you went on Friday night?

Prepositions

7 Complete the sentences with the correct preposition from the box.

up ~~at~~ in by to out in about

a I looked ..at.......... my watch: it was nearly ten o'clock.
b Linda woke .... at 9 o'clock.
c The story is that Robin Hood gave all his money .... poor people.
d Michael and Kate fell .... love when they were at university.
e The Prince lived .... an old castle in the mountains.
f I had a lot of work to do on Sunday, so I didn't go ....
g The author Jane Wilson wrote a book .... her journey to Africa.
h How did you travel to Mexico? – We went .... plane.

Pronunciation

Past forms

8 **a)** Listen to the pronunciation of the past forms on the recording. Notice how the pronunciation of the sound **in bold** is the same.

/æ/	h**a**d	beg**a**n	drank..........	....	....
/e/	r**ea**d	f**e**ll	....	....	
/ɔː/	c**augh**t	b**ough**t	....	....	....
/ʌ/	c**u**t	sh**u**t	....		

b) What is the past form of the verbs in the box? Put them in one of the above groups according to the pronunciation of the past form.

~~drink~~ leave meet run see sing think wear win

c) Listen to the pronunciation of words on the recording. Practise saying them.

Vocabulary booster: books, magazines and newspapers

9 a) Label the pictures with the words from the box.

headline	article	front page
~~newspaper~~	~~magazine~~	picture
advertisement	pages	cover
title	author	~~book~~

1 *newspaper*..........

2 ....

3 ....

4 ....

5 *magazine*..........

6 ....

7 ....

8 ....

9 *book*..........

10 ....

11 ....

12 ....

DAILY NEWS

JANUARY 25th, 2001 www.daily.news.co.uk

Newspaper of the Year

WOMAN WITH A MISSION

BOB JOHNSON'S NATIONWIDE QUEST FOR FEMALE FINANCIAL ADVICE

New sales blow hits Superstores

Poor Christmas profits deepen gloom for Superstore

By Tom Barley

INSIDE: JERRY WILSON 4-5 • SHOPPING 11 • SHARES & MARKET PRICES 12-13

The Image

WHAT'S HOT THIS SUMMER

Now the nights are getting lighter, it's time to turn on the heat. No problem – just grab a brush and comb, and style your hair to these top styles...

Hair styles this summer are the hottest we've seen for ages. Treat yourself to a look that will turn heads.

YOUR LETTERS

FASHION NEWS FROM NEW YORK

New! Silver Shine Nail Varnish

page 12

TREASURE ISLAND

ROBERT LOUIS STEVENSON

b) Listen to the pronunciation of the words on the recording. Practise saying them.

Listen and read

10 **a)** Read and listen to the text about these heroes/heroines.

National heroes and heroines

Mustafa Kemal Atatürk

Mustafa Kemal Atatürk is the father of modern Turkey. He was born in 1881. He chose the army as a career and in 1915, during the First World War, he led the Turkish army at Gelibolu and Istanbul. By the end of the war he was a hero and from that time on all of the Turkish people supported him. He led the Turkish army in the War of Independence (1919 - 1922) and in 1923 he became the first President of the new Republic of Turkey. During the last fifteen years of his life Atatürk introduced many reforms and did many things to improve life in Turkey. He died in November 1938, but today the people of Turkey still think of him with great respect.

Florence Nightingale

A hundred and fifty years ago, most nurses did not study nursing: but a British woman called Florence Nightingale tried to change all that. In the 1850s, she worked in a hospital for wounded soldiers in the Crimea (now Ukraine). People say she never slept, but spent all her time helping the men. The soldiers called her 'The Lady of the Lamp' because of the lamp she always carried as she walked around at night. When she returned to England, she began a school of nursing in London. She died in 1910.

Glossary *wounded* = hurt in a battle or war
Gelibolu = Gallipoli

b) Write the questions for the answers, as in the example.

1 *When was Atatürk born?*
In 1881.

2 ....
He led the Turkish army at Gelibolu and Istanbul.

3 ....
In 1923.

4 ....
In 1938.

5 ....
In the 1850s.

6 ....
'The Lady of the Lamp'.

7 ....
When she returned to England.

Improve your writing

A diary

11 **a)** Ray is a young Australian on holiday in Europe. He decided to travel from London to Prague by bus. Read his holiday diary and put the phrases below in the best place.

a ~~in the evening~~ b I didn't have any German money
c the bus wasn't there d and listened to the music
e only cost £50 f we finally left London
g When we arrived in France h I walked back to the car park
i was in another country

Sunday

Today was my last day in London. I spent the afternoon walking around, and (1) ....a.... I met two of my friends in a place called the Southern Lights, near Victoria Station. We talked (2) ....
I felt sorry to leave London, but everybody says Prague is a really beautiful city. I went home early – about ten o'clock – and packed my suitcase for tomorrow. London to Prague is 22 hours on the bus – it's a long journey, but my ticket (3) ....

Monday

We left Victoria Coach Station at about 1 o'clock. The bus was full of people, mostly young. There were one or two Australians and a lot of other nationalities too! The traffic was really bad at that time and it was nearly an hour before (4) ....
We arrived in Dover in the afternoon and took the ferry across the English Channel. (5) .... they asked to see my passport ... and then they told me I needed to pay for a visa!!

Tuesday

I fell asleep somewhere in the north of France ...
I felt so tired and when I woke up I (6) .... !!
The motorway was full of big German cars and everybody drove at about 150 kph!! About 10 o'clock, we stopped at a motorway service station, and I went into the shop for something to eat and drink. Then I remembered (7) .... to pay for it. In the end, a very kind person changed my US$ into German Marks for me, and I bought something to eat and drink. Twenty minutes later, (8) .... Life was good: I had food, drink and it was only four more hours to Prague. There was only one problem ... (9) .... !!

b) Complete Ray's diary with words from the box.

~~were~~ drove opened sat spoke thought
got stopped helped saw started said
remembered told ~~was~~

I was in a complete panic. My bag, my clothes and my passport (1) ....were.... all on the bus, the bus (2) ....was.... on the motorway ... and I was at the motorway service station. I (3) .... down by the road, thinking, 'What can I do? Help!!'
And soon someone (4) .... me. A kind German woman – who (5) .... perfect English – asked me if there was a problem.
I (6) .... her about the bus, and she (7) .... she could help me.
We (8) .... into her big German car – it was a Mercedes – and we (9) .... along the motorway at about 180 kilometres an hour.
A few minutes later, we (10) .... the bus – my bus. My new German friend (11) .... her window and (12) .... shouting 'Stop!! Stop!!' at the bus driver (in German, of course!!).
At first, the bus driver (13) .... she was crazy and drove faster ... until he saw me.
Perhaps he (14) .... my face. Then we drove along together until the next motorway service station, and then we both (15) ....

module 9

Adjectives: opposites

1 Write the opposite of:

a an expensive hotel
a cheap hotel ....

b a difficult question
....

c a big country
....

d an attractive face
....

e an old bicycle
....

f a comfortable chair
....

g a slow train
....

Comparative adjectives

2 Add the correct letters to make the comparative form of the adjectives below.

a young *e r*

b eas _ _ _

c big _ _ _

d cheap _ _

e health _ _ _

f new _ _

g happ _ _ _

h slim _ _ _

i quiet _ _

j hot _ _ _

3 **a)** Read the two facts, then write a sentence using the comparative form of the adjective.

1 The area of Brazil is 8.5 million km^2
The area of Australia is 7.6 million km^2
Brazil is bigger than Australia. ....
.... *(big)*

2 The River Volga in Russia is 3,500 km long.
The River Mississippi in the USA is 6,000 km long.
....
.... *(long)*

3 Blue whales usually weigh about 130 tonnes.
Elephants usually weigh about 7 tonnes.
....
.... *(heavy)*

4 The Pyramids in Egypt are about 4,000 years old.
The Parthenon in Greece is about 2,500 years old.
....
.... *(old)*

5 The World Trade Center, New York, is 415 m tall.
The Sears Tower in Chicago is 443 m tall.
....
.... *(tall)*

6 The Akashi-Kaikyo Bridge in Japan is nearly 2,000 m long.
The Sydney Harbour Bridge in Australia is 500 m long.
....
.... *(long)*

7 The price of gold is about $8,000 per kilo.
The price of silver is about $150 per kilo.
....
.... *(expensive)*

8 English has more than a hundred irregular verbs.
Esperanto has no irregular verbs!
....
.... *(easy)*

b) Listen to the sentences on the recording and practise saying them.

Superlative adjectives

4 **a)** Read the information about the Olympic athletes below.

Roy Seagrove -
Rower
Age: 38
Height: 1 m 90
Weight: 95 kg
These are his fifth Olympic Games
Three Olympic medals up to now

Jim Bowen -
Basketball player
Age: 19
Height: 1 m 95
Weight: 89 kg
First Olympic Games
Started playing basketball three months ago

Lilian Kay -
Marathon runner
Age: 25
Height: 1 m 60
Weight: 51 kg
Silver medal in the last Olympics

Karina Green -
Swimmer
Age: 16
Height: 1 m 72
Weight: 57 kg
First Olympic Games

b) Complete the sentences as in the example.

1 *Roy Seagrove* is *the oldest* .... (*old*)
2 .... is .... (*young*)
3 .... has got .... hair. (*long*)
4 .... has got .... hair. (*short*)
5 .... is .... (*tall*)
6 .... is .... (*heavy*)
7 .... is .... (*small*)
8 .... is .... (*successful*)

5 Change the adjective into the superlative form. Can you answer the questions?

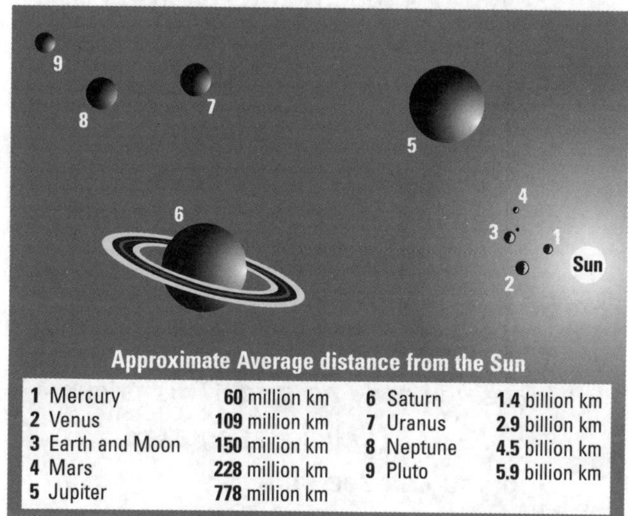

Approximate Average distance from the Sun

1 Mercury	**60** million km	**6** Saturn	**1.4** billion km
2 Venus	**109** million km	**7** Uranus	**2.9** billion km
3 Earth and Moon	**150** million km	**8** Neptune	**4.5** billion km
4 Mars	**228** million km	**9** Pluto	**5.9** billion km
5 Jupiter	**778** million km		

a Which is *the nearest*.............. (*near*) planet to the Sun? *Mercury*......
b What's the name of .... (*small*) planet? ....
c It's got over thirty moons and it's .... (*big*) planet in the solar system. ....
d Which is .... (*hot*) planet? ....
e This is the .... (*far*) planet from the Sun, and also .... (*cold*). ....
f Which planet is .... (*easy*) to see from the Earth? ....
g Which planet is .... (*close*) to Earth? ....

Comparative and superlative adjectives

6 **a)** Complete the joke with the comparative or superlative forms of the adjectives.

A woman went into (1) *the most expensive* (expensive) butcher's in town and asked for (2) .... (big) chicken in the shop. The shopkeeper showed her a chicken and said 'This is (3) .... (good) chicken in the shop, madam.' 'It's very small,' she said. 'Have you got a (4) .... (large) one?' 'Just a moment,' said the shopkeeper. He took the chicken into another room. In fact it was the only chicken he had. So he put some sausages inside to make it look (5) .... (big). 'Here you are,' he said. 'This is our (6) .... (delicious) chicken. And you can see that it's (7) .... (big) than the other. But I'm afraid it's also (8) .... (expensive).' 'Hmm ... but I'm not sure if it's (9) .... (good) than the other. OK. Can I have both of them, please?'

b) Listen to the joke on the recording.

Vocabulary

Shops and shopping

7 **a)** Rearrange the letters to make the names of shops.

1 You buy steak at a *butchers* BRUSHTEC
2 You buy shirts, trousers and skirts at a .... LOSHCET POSH
3 You buy newspapers, magazines and cigarettes at a .... SWEETGANNS
4 You buy things in the open air at a .... TRESTE TRAMEK
5 You buy books at a .... KOSHPOOB
6 You buy bread at a .... SKERAB
7 You buy fruit and vegetables at a .... CORNERSEGGER
8 You can buy stamps and send parcels at a .... STOP COFFEI
9 You can buy medicine at a .... HARMYCAP
10 You can buy almost everything at a .... SUETKRAMPER

b) Listen to the sentences on the recording. Practise saying them.

Pronunciation

Comparatives

8 **a)** Listen to the pronunciation of the adjectives below. Practise saying them.

big	old
fast	expensive
slow	difficult

b) Listen to the comparative forms. Notice the pronunciation of *than*. Practise saying them.

bigger than	older than
faster than	more expensive than
slower than	more difficult than

c) Listen to the sentences. Tick (✓) the true ones and cross (✗) the false ones.

1 Cats are bigger than tigers.
2 Trains are faster than aeroplanes.
3 Bicycles are slower than motorbikes.
4 New York is older than Rome.
5 Gold is more expensive than silver.
6 Driving a car is more difficult than riding a bicycle.

One and *ones*

9 Rewrite the sentences. Change the words in **bold** to *one* or *ones*.

a I don't have my old car now. I bought a new **car** last week.
I bought a new *one last week*.

b Martha has got three children. The youngest **child** is nearly three.
The youngest ....

c Your shoes are much more expensive than the **shoes** I bought.
Your shoes are much more expensive than
....

d 'Which colour pen would you like?'
'The red **pen**, please.'
The red ....

e There are many old buildings in the town centre. These **buildings** are the oldest.
These ....

Improve your writing

Describing a place

10 **a)** Complete this paragraph about *My Favourite Shop* with phrases from the box.

it sells	is open	The best time to go is
~~My favourite shop is~~	until eight o'clock at night	
The reason I like it is	The people there	

My Favourite Shop

(1) *My Favourite Shop is* called Talad Thai. It's in Putney, in south London. It's next to a Chinese restaurant, and (2) .... all kinds of food from China, Thailand and many other countries in the Far East.

(3) .... because I love cooking, especially oriental food. The shop (4) .... seven days a week, from ten o'clock in the morning (5) ....
(6) .... on a Sunday morning, when the shop is usually very quiet. (7) .... are always very friendly and they always try to help you find what you want.

b) Write a similar paragraph about a shop you know. Write about

- what the shop is called and where it is
- what it sells
- why you like it
- opening times
- the best time to go there
- the people there

Use some of the phrases from the box above.

Listen and read

11 Listen and read about three machines you can buy to make your life easier. Which machine is ...

a the most useful?
The Bryson D838 Robot Vacuum Cleaner ....

b the cheapest?
....

c the most useful for cooking ideas?
....

d the most expensive?
....

e the smallest?
....

f the best one for people who hate housework?
....

The three most intelligent machines for your home...

Thanks to computer chips, you can now buy machines that can think!!
Here are some of the best machines which can really make your life easier.

The Bryson D838 Robot Vacuum Cleaner

Do you like housework? No? Then this new robot vacuum cleaner is the machine for you. It can clean your living room automatically. It has a computer which tells it to go around objects such as chairs and table legs as it cleans your floor. And if a person – or your pet dog or cat – comes too close, it stops automatically. The Bryson D838 Robot Vacuum Cleaner comes with electric batteries, and costs £1,800.

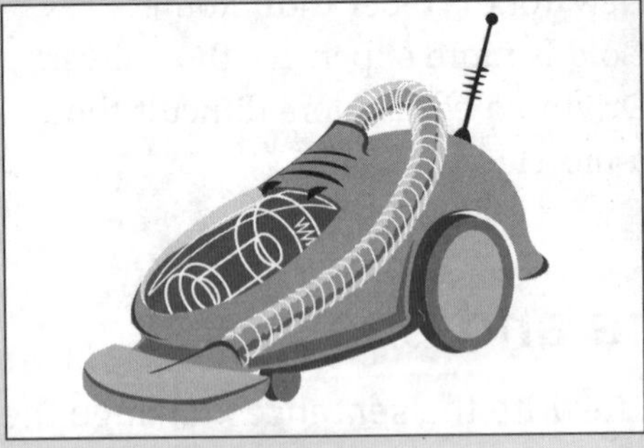

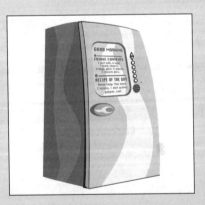

The Freezolux Smart Fridge

A fridge which tells you what it's got inside ... and gives you ideas about what to cook for dinner!! A visual display shows you what's inside the fridge – you don't even have to open the door, and the fridge can also tell when food is too old to use. And if you haven't got any ideas about what to cook for your family this evening ... just touch the computer screen on the door of the fridge, and you can look at over a thousand of your favourite recipes. You can also use it to send e-mails and to surf the Internet. The Freezolux Smart Fridge is more than just a fridge and costs only £999!

The Ultimate Power Control System

How many remote control units do you have in your house ... for the TV, the video, the CD player ... now you can control everything in your house – from a light in the bedroom to your front door – using just one special remote control unit. It works with radio signals so you can do everything in your house without getting out of bed. You can even surf the Internet, send e-mails, watch videos or listen to a CD with the Ultimate Power Control System's video screen. Price – £45. Buy now!!

Vocabulary booster: a supermarket

12 **a)** Label the things in the picture with words from the box.

~~checkout~~ cashier shopping list customer shopping trolley shopping basket till queue cans plastic bags

b) Listen to the pronunciation of the words on the recording. Practise saying them.

module 10

Spelling

-*ing* forms

> LOOK!
>
> most verbs
> add -*ing*
> *He's flying to Spain.*
>
> verbs ending in -*e*
> take away the -*e*
> *She's making dinner.*
>
> verbs ending consonant + vowel + consonant
> double the final consonant
> *She's sitting there.*

1 Write the -*ing* form of these verbs.

a read *reading*......
b study ....
c wash ....
d leave ....
e come ....
f stop ....
g look ....
h dance ....
i stay ....
j give ....
k plan ....
l drive ....

Present Continuous

2 **a)** Look at the picture. Write what the people are doing, using the verbs.

1 The robot *is cleaning*......... (*clean*) the living room.
2 Veronica .... (*look*) out of the window.
3 She .... (*talk*) to someone on her mobile phone.
4 The baby .... (*sit*) on the floor.
5 The baby .... (*eat*) the flowers.
6 Ronald .... (*have*) a cup of tea.
7 He .... (*watch*) television.
8 The two older children .... (*do*) their homework.

b) Listen to the sentences on the recording. Practise saying them.

Question words

3 **a)** Write the correct question words in the following sentences and match them to their answers in the box below.

1 *What*...... are you doing?
My homework...

2 .... are you going?
....

3 .... are you smiling?
....

4 .... are you talking to?
....

5 .... are you reading?
....

6 .... are you watching?
....

Because you look so funny! My brother. Oh, nothing, just a magazine. To my English class. Ssh!! It's my favourite programme. ~~My homework~~

b) Listen to the questions and answers on the recording. Practise saying them.

Short answers

4

LOOK!

Short answers with the Present Continuous

Are you going home?	Yes, **I am/we are.** No, **I'm/we're not.**
Are they going home?	Yes, **they are.** No, **they aren't.**
Is he/she listening?	Yes, **he/she is.** No, **he/she isn't.**

Notice! We do not use contracted forms in **positive** short answers.

Yes, I am. **not** ~~*Yes, I'm*~~.

Write short answers to these questions.

a Are you enjoying the party, Jo?
Yes, I am...........

b Is it raining outside?
No, ...

c Are your friends staying in this hotel?
Yes, ...

d Are you two coming with us?
Yes, ...

e Are you waiting to see the doctor, madam?
No, ...

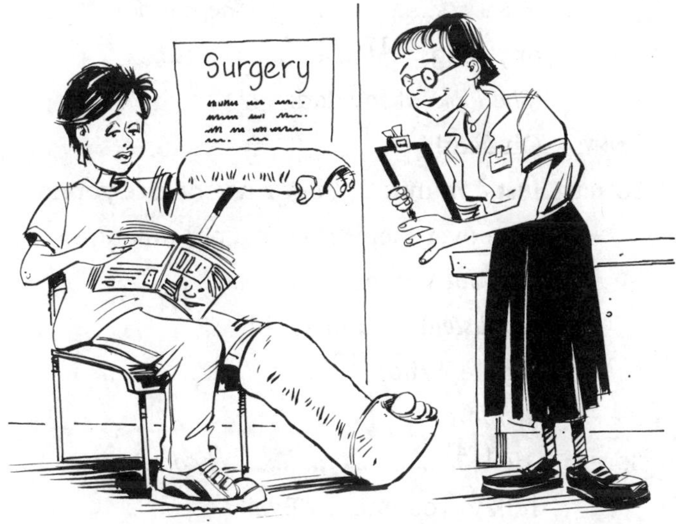

f Is Thomas driving?
Yes, ...

g Is she talking to us?
No, ...

All forms

5 **a)** Put the verb in brackets into the correct form of the Present Continuous: positive, negative, question form or short answer.

SOPHIE: It's me, Sophie.

JENNY: Hi, Sophie. Where are you? What (1) *are you doing*......... (*you/do*)?

SOPHIE: I'm at my sister's wedding.

JENNY: Fantastic! (2) .... (*you/enjoy*) yourself?

SOPHIE: No, (3) ....!! (4) .... (*I/not/have*) a good time. It's awful!!

JENNY: Why? What (5) .... (*happen*)?

SOPHIE: Well, there's the music for a start. (6) .... (*They/play*) this awful 80s music ... and ... oh no, I don't believe it ... my dad (7) .... (*dance*) with my mum's sister.

JENNY: How about your mum? (8) .... (*she/dance*) too?

SOPHIE: No, (9) .... (10) .... (*She/not/do*) anything. (11) .... (*She/look*) at my dad.

JENNY: Oh dear!!

SOPHIE: Just a minute ... there's a very nice young man over there. There's a girl talking to him but (12) he .... (*not/listen*) ... and ... oh!!

JENNY: Sophie. What (13) .... (*he/do*)?

SOPHIE: He (14) .... (*come*) over ... Talk to you later ... 'Bye!!

b) Listen to the conversation on the recording.

Present Continuous and Present Simple

6 Underline the best form of the verb, Present Simple or Present Continuous.

a Can I speak to Jane Parsons, please?
– Sorry, she's not in the office today. *She works/She's working* at home today.

b Where *do you come/are you coming* from?
– I'm Italian ... from Milan.

c *Do you speak/Are you speaking* Japanese?
– Just a little.

d Don't forget your umbrella! *It's raining/It rains* again.

e Can you help me with the dinner?
– Not now ... *I watch/I'm watching* TV.

f In Britain, cars *drive/are driving* on the left.

g Hello!! What *do you do/are you doing* here?
– *I'm waiting/I wait* for a friend.

h Can I look at the newspaper now? *Are you reading/Do you read* it?

i Can I phone you back later? *We're having/We have* dinner.

Vocabulary

Describing people

7 Match the words on the right to the definitions on the left.

a	A piece of jewellery that you wear on your ear.	1	tall
b	A head where all – or nearly all – the hair is cut.	2	dark
c	The hair on a man's face under his mouth.	3	good-looking
d	Attractive: nice to look at.	4	glasses
e	(for a person) The opposite of small or short.	5	shaved
f	Thin, in a good way.	6	blonde
g	You wear these if you can't see very well.	7	~~earring~~
h	Hair which is yellow or light-coloured.	8	ponytail
i	You use them to see things.	9	slim
j	The hair on a man's face above his mouth.	10	beard
k	Hair which is brown or black.	11	moustache
l	Hair which you tie together at the back of your head.	12	eyes

a ..7.......... d .... g .... j ....
b .... e .... h .... k ....
c .... f .... i .... l ....

's

8 **a)** Write 's in the correct place in the Column A sentences below.

	A	B
1	My sister's in her mid-twenties.	...is........
2	Everybody says she very good-looking.	....
3	Where Frank going?	....
4	Who the girl with long dark hair?	....
5	Dina got short hair.	....
6	David mother doesn't wear glasses.	....
7	Ann the black girl with medium-length hair.	....
8	Maria waiting for me in the car.	....
9	My father got a moustache.	....
10	What colour are Barbara earrings?	....

b) Is 's: *is*, *has* or possessive in each sentence? Complete Column B.

Vocabulary

Clothes

9 Look at the pictures of Bob, Paul and Marie.
Who is wearing ...

a trainers? ..Bob..........
b a skirt? ....
c a coat? ....
d a tie? ....
e black shoes? ....
f earrings? ....
g a shirt? ....
h jeans? ....
i a suit? ....
j trousers? ....
k a white jacket? ....
l a pullover? ....

Listen and read

10 Read and listen to the text about street style, and complete the table.

	Where is she from?	What clothes does she talk about?	Where did she buy her clothes?
Mina	London		
Gloria		dress, trousers, shoes	
Alice			Milan, New York

Street Style

This week we went to South Molton Street to find out what young people are wearing when they go shopping.

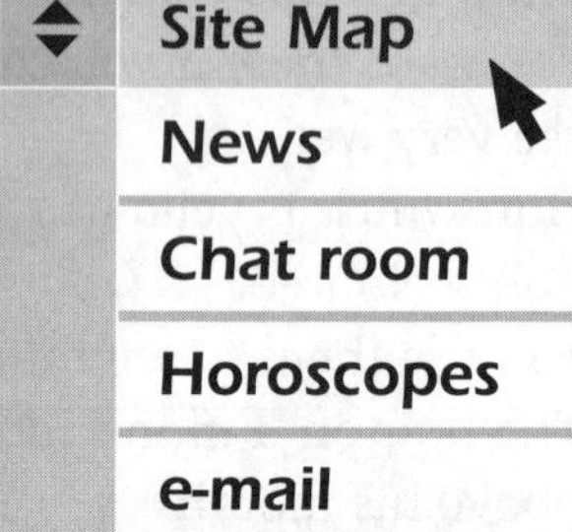

Mina is from London: she's a student at the London College of Fashion.

'I'm wearing a pair of jeans from *Michiko* - it's a Japanese shop here in London.'

'I love Japanese clothes. The jumper is from *Space*, and I bought the jacket at Camden Market a couple of weeks ago. My bag and shoes were presents from my family. I like wearing clothes that are different, so I don't usually go shopping in big shops.'

Gloria is a designer from Barcelona, in Spain. She's spending a few days here in London. 'Because I'm a designer, I love making clothes for myself. I made this dress, and these trousers, too. My shoes are from Spain, too ... they're my favourite shoes, but I can't remember where I bought them!'

'I'm looking for a bag which looks good with these clothes. I love shopping in London, but it's very expensive!'

Alice is from the United States. She works for an airline company. 'I travel a lot because of my job: I love my work because I can go shopping in lots of wonderful places.'

'I bought this top in Milan, and my trousers and shoes are from New York. As well as Italy and the United States, I love shopping here in London, too. I'm going to a shop called *Puzzle* - it's near here - to buy myself a new jacket.'

Improve your writing

Correcting mistakes

11 Read the description of the picture.
There are twelve mistakes underlined: correct them.

There (a) is five people in the picture. They are all (b) siting outside: it's a nice day and the sun is (c) shineing. Perhaps they (d) is all on holiday together. One of the men is (e) wearring a suit. One man is behind the others: (f) she's reading a book. The woman in the front (g) have got a newspaper, but she (h) don't reading it. Her (i) eye are closed: perhaps (j) she sleeping. I like this picture: the people (k) looks calm and happy and the scenery is very (l) atractive.

Pronunciation

Stress in questions

12 **a)** Listen to the pronunciation of the question words, and the questions with the Present Continuous.

1 What — What are you doing?
2 What — What are they doing?
3 What — What's he doing? What's she doing?
4 Where — Where are you going?
5 Where — Where are they going?
6 Where — Where's he going? Where's she going?

b) Listen again and practise saying the questions.

module 11

can/can't for ability

1 **a)** Look at the information about four students: Caroline, Fabrizio, Kristina and Max.

	speak French	play chess	drive a car	play a musical instrument
Caroline	✓	✗	✗	✓
Fabrizio	✓	✓	✗	✗
Kristina	✗	✗	✓	✓
Max	✗	✓	✓	✗

b) Complete the sentences about Caroline and Fabrizio.

1 Caroline *can*.............................. speak French.
2 She *can't*.............................. play chess.
3 .... drive a car.
4 .... play a musical instrument.
5 Fabrizio ....
6 He ....
7 ....
8 ....

c) Listen to the sentences on the recording. Practise saying them.

Questions and short answers

2

> LOOK!
>
> Short answers with *can/can't*
>
> **Can** I/you/he/she/we/they **ask a question?**
>
> **Yes**, I/you/he/she/we/they **can**.
> **No**, I/you/he/she/we/they **can't**.

a) Look back at the information about Kristina and Max. Write the questions and short answers.

1 *Can Kristina speak French?*
No, she can't.
2 ....
....
3 ....
....
4 ....
....
5 ....
....
6 ....
....
7 ....
....
8 ....
....

b) Listen to the questions and answers on the recording. Practise saying them.

Question words

3 Complete the questions below with the correct question word(s) from the box.

~~Where~~ What kind How What time What colour What When Which

a *Where*.......... is Brisbane?
It's in Australia.

b .... of tree is that?
It's a palm tree.

c .... did you go to South America?
Four years ago.

d .... is your coat?
The black one.

e .... is your new car?
White.

f .... do we arrive in New York?
At about three o'clock.

g ....'s your sister's name?
Maria.

h .... do I switch this off?
Press the red button.

4 a) Read the text below.

Ships of the desert

Perhaps they aren't the most beautiful animals in the world ... but in the hot lands of North Africa and the Middle East they are certainly one of the most useful. But how much do you know about camels?

Camels normally live for about 40 years – but they usually stop working when they are about 25.

Camels don't normally like running – it's too hot – but when they need to, they can run at 20 kilometres an hour. The dromedary, or Arabian camel has one hump. The Bactrian, or Asian camel, has longer hair and has got two humps. There are about 14 million camels in the world, and most of them are dromedaries.

An adult camel is about 2.1 metres tall and weighs about 500 kilograms. Camels can walk for more than 600 kilometres without drinking. They only need to drink water every six or eight days. But when there is water, they can drink up to 90 litres.

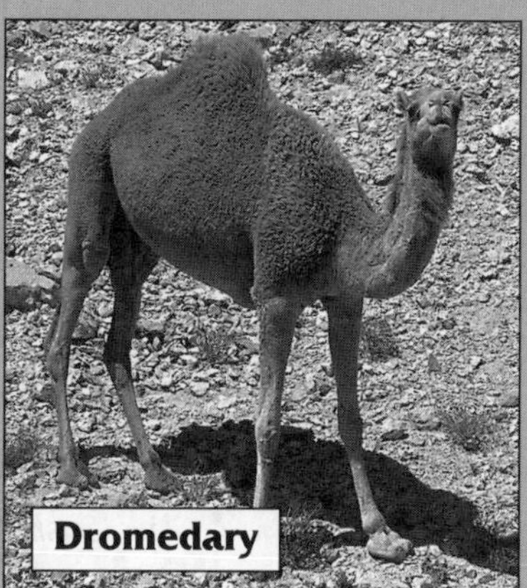

Dromedary

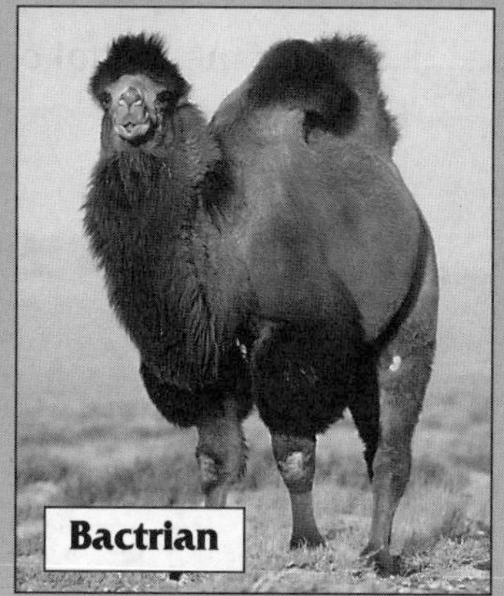

Bactrian

b) Write the questions for this information.

1 *How long do camels live?*
For about 40 years.
2 How ....
About twenty kilometres an hour.
3 How ....
One.
4 How ....
14 million.
5 How ....
2.1 metres.
6 How ....
About 500 kilograms.
7 How ....
More than 600 kilometres.
8 How ....
Every six or eight days.
9 How ....
Up to 90 litres.

5 Complete the sentences with *how much*, *how many*, *which* or *what*.

a *What*........... do you study at university?
b .... aunts and uncles have you got?
c There's chocolate or vanilla ice cream for dessert. .... do you prefer?
d .... milk do you want in your coffee?
e There's a bus at nine o'clock and another one at eleven o'clock. .... is better for you?
f .... time did you spend in Africa?
g .... people were there at the meeting?
h .... does a kilo of cheese cost?
i .... is the capital of Romania?

Word order in questions

6 Put the words in the questions into the correct order.

a are there – in – How – many – the USA – states ?
How many states are there in the USA?
b did – films – How many – make – he ?
....
c a football match – does – How – last – long ?
....
d the boxer – Muhammad Ali – born – was – Where ?
....
e it from – How far – here – to your home – is ?
....
f do – of – What kind – like – you – music ?
....
g can – a – cheetah – fast – run – How ?
....
h the world – is – in – the biggest – ocean – What ?
....

Articles

7 The questions below all come from the general knowledge quiz on page 94 of the Students' Book. Complete the questions with *a*, *an* or *the*.

a Where was .*the*..... Hollywood actor Arnold Schwarzenegger born?
b How many players are there in .... basketball team?
c How long does it take to boil .... egg?
d When did Bill Clinton become President of .... United States?
e What is .... biggest desert in .... world?
f When did Joseph Niépce invent .... first camera?
g How far is it from .... Earth to .... Moon?
h When did France win .... World Cup?
i *Sushi* is .... popular type of food. Where does it come from?

Vocabulary booster: animals

8 **a)** How many of the animals below can you name? Write the word next to the correct number below.

duck	frog	mouse	dog	cow	sheep	monkey	horse	bees	beetle	snake	spider

1 .... 5 .... 9 ....

2 .... 6 .... 10 ....

3 .... 7 .... 11 ....

4 .... 8 .... 12 ....

b) Listen to the pronunciation of the words on the recording. Practise saying them.

c) Put the animals into one of the groups below.

Animals with no legs ..... *snake*

Animals with two legs ....

Animals with four legs ....
....

Animals with more than four legs ....

Listen and read

9 Read and listen to the text about the animal world, and find out:

a About how many animals species are there in the world? *ten million*

b How tall can an adult giraffe grow? ....

c How long is the smallest mammal, Savi's pygmy shrew? ....

d How much does a goliath frog weigh? ....

e How tall is an adult ostrich? ....

f How fast can a bee hummingbird move its wings? ....

g How many types of kangaroo are there? ....

h How many bison were/are there in America in:

i) the 1860s ....

ii) the 1880s ....

iii) now? ....

The Animal World

We do not know how many species of animal there are, as people are discovering new ones all the time; but most scientists think that there are about ten million different animal species in the world.

Giraffes are the tallest animals on Earth. A large adult male giraffe can be up to 6 metres tall. Thanks to its long legs and neck, it can eat the leaves from the tops of trees.

The smallest animals are called protozoa, which have only one cell, and are so small that we cannot see them without a powerful microscope.

The smallest mammal is Savi's pygmy shrew – it is only 6 centimetres long, including its tail.

The goliath frog (*Rana Goliath*) of West Africa can be up to 75 centimetres long, and weighs about 3 kilograms. The goliath beetle is probably the world's largest beetle – it weighs more than 100 grams – about the same as two eggs.

Protozoa

Shrew

Ostrich

Hummingbird

Bison

The ostrich is the world's largest bird. An adult ostrich is more than 2.5 metres tall, but it cannot fly.

The bee hummingbird is probably the world's smallest bird – it is just 5 centimetres long and weighs less than 2 grams: it can stay still in the air by moving its wings twenty to fifty times a second. One of the largest birds which can fly is the South American condor: its wings are three metres from end to end.

There are more than fifty different types of kangaroo in Australia. When it is born, a baby kangaroo is less than 2.5 centimetres long: but an adult kangaroo can grow to more than 2 metres in height.

In the mid-1860s, there were about 13 million bison living in North America. By the mid-1880s, there were only a few hundred. Today there are about 50,000 bison in America, living in special parks.

More about numbers

10 **a)** Put the words into numbers.

1 sixty thousand 60,000
2 nineteen eighty-five ....
3 three thousand ....
4 ninety kilometres an hour ....
5 nine point six ....
6 two hundred and fifty-three thousand ....
7 sixty-two million ....
8 two hundred and ninety-seven ....
9 two billion ....
10 nine hundred and sixty-three ....

b) Put the numbers into words.

1 53,000 fifty-three thousand
2 150km/h ....
3 3,000,000 ....
4 8.5 ....
5 348 ....
6 2,000,000,000 ....
7 5,600 ....
8 1980 ....
9 350,000 ....
10 80,000,000 ....

Pronunciation

Numbers

11 **a)** Listen to the pronunciation of these words. Practise saying them.

nine	nineteen	hundred	thousand
million	billion		

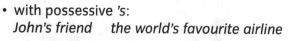

b) Listen to the pronunciation of the numbers in Exercise 10a. Practise saying them.

c) Practise saying the words in Exercise 10b. Listen to the recording to check.

Improve your writing

Full stops, apostrophes and question marks

12

LOOK!

We use apostrophes:
- in contracted forms:
  she's can't doesn't

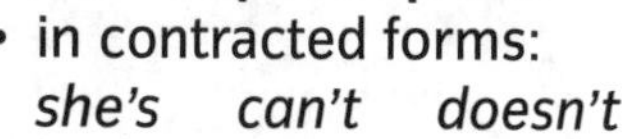

- with possessive *'s*:
  John's friend the world's favourite airline

We use full stops at the end of statements.
They're French. I'm fine.

We use question marks at the end of questions.
Where do you live? Where is it?

Write apostrophes, full stops and question marks in the sentences below.

a Dogs can only see black and white: they can't see colours.
b Im not sure what the answer is
c Is it true that koala bears dont drink water
d What is the worlds largest animal
e He doesnt know the answer
f Wheres the biggest lake in the world
g What is Peters pet dogs name

module 12

Future plans

going to

1 **a)** Look at the pictures and write a sentence about what the people are going to do. Use the phrases in the box.

have lunch ~~have a baby~~ stop get wet buy a newspaper paint the ceiling go to bed play tennis

1 *She's going to have a baby.*

2 He ....

3 They ....

4 The bus ....

5 They ....

6 He ....

7 They ....

8 They ....

b) Listen to the answers on the recording. Practise saying them.

want to

2 Complete the sentences with the correct form of *want to*: positive, question or negative. Use the words in brackets.

a *Do you want to*.......... (*you*) rent a video this evening? There's nothing good on TV.

b No, I'm really not hungry. .... (*I*) eat anything, thank you.

c Valerie is going to look for a job when she leaves school. .... (*she*) go to university.

d .... (*anybody*) go for a cup of coffee when the lesson finishes?

e .... (*your friends*) go for a walk before we have dinner?

f Patricia is very, very tired. .... (*she*) go home and go to bed.

g .... (*he*) be a waiter, but it was the only job he could find.

h .... (*you*) anything to eat with your coffee?

would like to and *want to*

3 **a)** Rearrange the words to make sentences with *want to* or *would like to*.

1 would like – a footballer – to be – when he's older – Stephen
Stephen would like to be a footballer when he's older.

2 you – something – like – to drink? – Would
....

3 and I – a table – near – My friends – the window, please – would like
....

4 want – doesn't – stay – at home – to – Marc
....

5 this evening? – to see – like – film – Which – would you
....

6 a – taxi – order – I'd – to – please – like
....

7 coffee, – We – thank you – any more – want – don't
....

8 in the park? – you – Would – like – to go – for a walk
....

b) Listen to the sentences on the recording. Practise saying them.

Future forms

4 Write **one** extra word in the sentences below.

a Françoise *would* like to go to Japan one day.

b Tomorrow's Saturday ... I going to stay in bed all day.

c Where do you want go?

d Would you to go out for lunch?

e Chris isn't enjoying his holiday: he to go home!!

f My friends are going cook a special meal this evening.

g What would you like do tomorrow?

h We not going to have a holiday this year.

Vocabulary

Ways to spend the weekend

5 Complete the words to make words or phrases to express the opposite.

a	It was boring!	It was g *o o* d f *u* n!
b	a busy weekend	a q _ _ _ t weekend.
c	a relaxing day	a t _ _ _ _ g day
d	stay in	go _ _ _
e	get up	s _ _ y in b _ _
f	never	a _ _ _ _ s

Word combinations with *go*, *have*, *stay*

6 Find the correct words or phrases in the box.

a concert	a novel	the gym
~~children~~	television	at home
in bed	sport	an exhibition
a museum	the cinema	

a who can you **look after**?
children ....

b what five things can you **go to**?
....
....
....
....
....

c where can you **stay** (two places)?
....
....

d what can you **watch** (two things)?
....
....

e what can you can **read**?
....

Suggestions and offers

7 **a)** Mark, Barbara and their two children are on a camping holiday in the mountains. Complete the conversation with one of the words or phrases from the box.

~~shall~~	see	Let's	I'll	about	idea	could	like	we	don't want

MARK: Well, everybody ... what (1) *shall* .... we do today? Any ideas?

SUSIE: I'm not sure ... it depends on the weather. Is it sunny outside?

MARK: Just a minute ... no, not exactly ... in fact, it's raining again.

JAKE: Oh no! I (2) .... another boring day like yesterday. Is there something interesting we can go and see?

BARBARA: I know what we can do. (3) .... have a look at the guide book. I'm sure we can find some ideas in there.

MARK: All right. Where is the guide book?

SUSIE: It's there, next to your feet.

MARK: Let's (4) .... well, there's the Museum of Country Life; how (5) .... that?

JAKE: Hmm ... is there anything more exciting?

MARK: Well, we (6) .... go to *Aqua World*. It's a Sea Life centre.

JAKE: Yes, that sounds better. Shall (7) .... go there?

SUSIE: OK then, if you (8) ....

BARBARA: Shall I phone them to see what time it opens?

MARK: Good (9) ....! So everybody's happy. (10) .... make some more coffee and then we can all get ready.

b) Listen to the conversation and check your answers.

Pronunciation

I'll, we'll

8 a) Listen to the pairs of sentences below. Notice the pronunciation of *'ll*.

1	I open the window.	I'll open the window.
2	I turn on the heating.	I'll turn on the heating.
3	We make lunch for you.	We'll make lunch for you.
4	I phone for a taxi.	I'll phone for a taxi.
5	I drive.	I'll drive.
6	We buy some bread.	We'll buy some bread.

b) Practise saying the sentences. Copy the voices.

Future time expressions

9 a) It is 9 a.m. on Wednesday. Write the future time expressions in order.

tonight	~~this afternoon~~	tomorrow evening	next month	next year
tomorrow morning	next week	this weekend		

9 a.m. Wednesday

this afternoon........

....

....

....

....

....

....

....

b) It is now 4 p.m. on Friday, April 10th 2001. What's another way to say ...

1 10 a.m., Saturday April 11th? ....

2 9 p.m., Saturday? ....

3 The week 13–17th April? ....

4 Saturday and Sunday, April 11th and 12th? ....

5 May 2001? ....

6 2002? ....

7 10 p.m. Friday April 10th? ....

Talking about the weather

10 Read the sentences and describe the weather.

a You're going to need your umbrellas if you go out.
It's raining./It's wet...............

b Can you pass me my sunglasses ... that's better. Now I can see!!
....

c Thirty-five degrees!! Let's go for a swim!
....

d Please drive carefully: in some places you can't see more than five metres.
....

e What a beautiful spring day. Let's go for a walk!
....

f The weather's not too bad today: there's no sun, but it isn't raining.
....

g Look outside! The garden is completely white!!
....

h Put on your warm clothes if you go out!
....

i All the leaves are falling off the trees!!
....

Prepositions

11 Complete the sentences with *in*, *on*, *to* or *at*.

a Paul never goes out .*at*...... the weekend.

b Let's go .... the cinema!

c There's a party .... my house on Saturday. Can you come?

d I'm so tired. I'm going to stay .... bed all day tomorrow.

e The weather can get really hot .... summer.

f I didn't go out at all this weekend: I just stayed .... home as usual.

g Martina and I went .... a rock concert on Saturday – it was great!

h We went to the United States .... holiday a few years ago.

Listen and read

12 Read and listen to the world weather report for the week ending 15th March. Complete the information in the table.

	What was the weather like?	Extra information
Chicago	*snow, windy*	....
San Francisco	....	....
Queensland	....	*475 mm of rain in five days*
Jerez de la Frontera	....	....
The Balkans	....	....
North-east Italy	....	....
Irkutsk	....	....

The World Weather Report

March 15th

There was heavy snow and windy weather in Chicago on Monday, and there was also heavy rain on the west coast of the United States – particularly in and around the city of San Francisco.

Things were no better on the other side of the world in Australia – there was extremely heavy rain in the state of Queensland, with 475 mm of rain falling in just five days.

In south-west Europe, there was more hot, sunny weather with the town of Jerez de la Frontera in the south of Spain the hottest place. The temperature was 30 degrees, the warmest so far this year.

It wasn't all good news in Europe however. There was heavy snow in the Balkans, and parts of north-eastern Italy on Monday and Tuesday. Things are getting a little better in the city of Irkutsk, in eastern Siberia, however: the temperature went above zero degrees for the first time since last November.

Vocabulary

Definitions

13 Use the definition to write in the word. You can find all the words in Module 12 of the Students' Book.

a A book which tells a story about imaginary people.
  N*OVEL*

b A place where people grow grapes.
  V _ _ _ _ _ _ _

c A place where you go for physical exercise.
  G _ _

d A time when people meet and enjoy themselves.
  P _ _ _ _

e A way of agreeing to a suggestion.
  GOOD I _ _ _!

f A way of making a suggestion.
  L _ _ ' _ GO!

g A word for people in your family.
  R _ _ _ _ _ _ _ _

h A word for Saturday and Sunday.
  W _ _ _ _ _ _

i Breakfast, lunch and dinner are all ...
  M _ _ _ _

j Extra work which you do after school.
  H _ _ _ _ _ _ _

k It means 'not interesting'.
  B _ _ _ _ _

l To take care of.
  LOOK A _ _ _ _

m This is between the afternoon and the night.
  E _ _ _ _ _ _

n This is what you do when you move through water using your arms and legs.
  S _ _ _

o This is when you go to hear people playing music.
  C _ _ _ _ _ _

p This is when you move your body to music.
  D _ _ _ _

q You see these at the cinema.
  F _ _ _ _

r You are this when you want to drink something.
  T _ _ _ _ _ _

Improve your writing

Write about a popular holiday place

14 **a)** Make notes about a popular holiday place in your country under these headings:

Where it is
The most important attractions
Places to eat and drink
Things to do for children
Excursions

b) Write a paragraph about the place using some of the phrases in the box.

... is in the north/south/east/west of ... It's one of the (oldest/most interesting/most beautiful) towns in ... It has a large number of ... The best ... is ... which has ... There are lots of places to ... You can enjoy ... For children there is ... You can also visit ...

module 13

Present Perfect

1 Complete the sentences with the Present Perfect form of the verbs in brackets.

a Karen's parents *have lived*......... in Scotland all their lives. (*live*)

b J.R. Cowling .... more than twenty books. (*write*)

c 60% of people in the United States .... never .... abroad. (*go*)

d Martin .... hundreds of e-mails to Kyla – she's his favourite singer. (*send*)

e My friend and I .... all of Steven Spielberg's films. (*see*)

f I .... never .... a Ferrari ... but I'd like to!! (*drive*)

g Because of her job, Diana .... a lot of famous people. (*meet*)

h Do you like Japanese food? – I don't know. I .... never .... it. (*try*)

Positive and negative

2 **a)** The first Women's Soccer World Cup was in China in 1991. There have been two more World Cups: here are the winners and the losing finalists.

Year	Venue	Winners	Goals	Losing finalists	Goals
1991	China	United States	2	Norway	1
1995	Sweden	Norway	2	Germany	0
1999	USA	United States (*United States won on penalties*)	0	China	0

b) Complete the sentences with the Present Perfect of the verb.

1 There *have been*......... (*be*) three World Cups up to now.

2 The United States .... (*win*) the competition twice.

3 They .... (*not/have*) the competition in South America.

4 Germany .... (*play*) in one World Cup Final.

5 The United States .... (*never/lose*) in the Final.

6 There .... (*be*) one World Cup in Europe.

7 Norway and the United States .... (*play*) in two finals.

8 Germany .... (*not/win*) the World Cup.

9 Norway .... (*score*) three goals in the World Cup Finals.

10 There .... (*be*) one final which finished in a penalty competition.

Questions and short answers

> **LOOK!**
> **Short answers with the Present Perfect**
> **Have** you/I/we/they **done it?**
> **Yes**, I/you/we/they **have**.
> **No**, I/you/we/they **haven't**.
>
> **Has** he/she/it **done it?**
> **Yes**, he/she/it **has**.
> **No**, he/she/it **hasn't**.

3 **a)** Read about the people below. Then complete the questions and write the correct short answer.

Richard Marshall and his wife Elaine are retired. Recently they moved to a new house in Hexham, a town near Newcastle, in the north of England. Richard was born in Hexham, but Elaine is originally from Aberdeen, a town in the north of Scotland.

Gordon Marshall – Richard and Elaine's son – was born in Newcastle but he now lives with his wife and daughter in Leeds, a town about 150 km away, where he is a teacher. He's also worked abroad: he worked in a restaurant in France when he was younger.

Sarah Marshall – Gordon's wife – has always wanted her own business. Her daughter Rebecca left school last year, and now they're in business together. She and her mother have opened a new sandwich shop called *Crusts* in Leeds city centre. It's the first time they've worked together!

1 *Has*.... Richard always lived in Hexham?
Yes, he has...........

2 .... Elaine ever lived in another town?
....

3 .... they always lived in the same house?
....

4 .... Gordon always been a teacher?
....

5 .... he ever worked abroad?
....

6 .... Gordon and Sarah always lived in Leeds?
....

7 .... Sarah had her own business before?
....

8 .... Rebecca left school?
....

b) Listen to the sentences on the recording. Practise saying them.

Irregular past participles

4 **a)** Find the past participles of the verbs. What is the mystery word?

sleep	*S*	*L*	*E*	*P*	*T*			
make			_	_	_	_		
lose		_	_	_	_			
stand			_	_	_	_	_	
speak			_	_	_	_	_	_
take			_	_	_	_	_	
drive			_	_	_	_	_	_
write	_	_	_	_	_	_	_	
say		_	_	_	_			
come				_	_	_	_	
give			_	_	_	_	_	
keep		_	_	_	_			
tell		_	_	_	_			
become			_	_	_	_	_	_
see				_	_	_	_	

b) Listen to the pronunciation of the verbs on the recording. Practise saying them.

Spelling
Regular past participles

5

> LOOK!
>
> To form the past participle of regular verbs we add *-ed*:
> ***play*** ➡ ***played***
>
> If the regular verb ends in *-e* we add *-d* only:
> ***decide*** ➡ ***decided***
>
> say and pay take *-aid*:
> ***say*** ➡ ***said***
> ***pay*** ➡ ***paid***
>
> Verbs ending in consonant + *-y* change the *-y* to *-ied*:
> ***study*** ➡ ***studied***
> ***try*** ➡ ***tried***

Look at the sentences below. Is the spelling of the past participle correct or not? If it is incorrect, write the correct spelling.

a Have you ever **staid** in an expensive hotel? ..*X*..
..*stayed*....

b Have you **used** this kind of computer before? .....
....

c I've never **tryed** Japanese tea before. It's delicious!! .....
....

d We haven't **decided** where to go on holiday. .....
....

e My mother has always **studyed** music. .....
....

f Exams have never **worried** me. .....
....

g Have you ever **plaid** baseball? .....
....

h I've **livd** in this apartment all my life. .....
....

ever, *before*, *never*, *always*

6
Complete the gaps with *always*, *before*, *ever* or *never*.

a I don't know what this is: I haven't eaten it ..*before*..........

b Laura has .... wanted to be a doctor: it's her ambition.

c Have you .... met anyone famous?

d Is this your first visit to Oxford.
– No, it isn't. I've been here ....

e I've .... liked pop music: I prefer jazz.

f Have you tried Indian food .... , or is this the first time?

g We're very happy with our car; we've .... had any problems with it.

h Have you .... slept outside all night?

Definite and zero article

7
Complete the sentences with *the* or Ø.

a We often have dinner in *Luigi's*: ..*the*..... pizzas are really good there.

b What was .... name of .... man who invented television?

c Did you see .... football match on TV last night?

d Which are usually cheaper? .... apples or .... oranges?

e Can I have a cup of tea, please? I don't drink .... coffee.

f I'm sorry, I can't hear you – .... music is too loud!!

g Do you take .... sugar in your coffee?

h We had a good holiday, but .... weather wasn't very good.

Articles: *a*, *an* and *the*

8 **a)** Complete the joke with *a*, *an* or *the*.

Once upon (1) *a*........ time there was (2) .... lion. He felt very happy with himself that day, so he decided to go for (3) .... walk in (4) .... jungle. After (5) .... few minutes, he met (6) .... snake.

'Who is (7) .... king of (8) .... jungle?' asked (9) .... lion.

'You are, of course,' replied (10) .... snake. (11) .... lion felt even happier.

Next, (12) .... lion came to (13) .... big river. Sitting in (14) .... river, there was (15) .... crocodile.

'Who is (16) .... king of the jungle?' (17) .... lion asked (18) .... crocodile.

'You are, of course,' answered (19) .... crocodile, and swam away.

(20) .... lion continued his walk. All (21) .... animals he met agreed that (22) .... lion was (23) .... king of (24) .... jungle.

Finally, he met (25) .... elephant.

'Who is (26) .... king of (27) .... jungle?' asked (28) .... lion.

(29) .... elephant didn't say anything, but he picked up (30) .... lion in his enormous trunk, and threw him into (31) .... air.

'All right, all right,' said (32) .... lion, 'Don't get angry just because you don't know (33) .... answer.'

b) Listen to the joke and check your answers.

Vocabulary

Ways of communicating

9 What are these instructions for? Choose one of the phrases from the box.

~~leaving a phone message~~	sending an e-mail
making a telephone call	buying online
surfing the Internet	sending a card
writing a letter	sending a fax

a 'After you hear a BEEP, speak slowly and clearly. Don't forget to say your name, ...'
leaving a phone message..

b Write your address and the date in the top right corner. Start with *Dear* and the name of the ...
....

c When you've finished your writing, click on the *Send* button at the top of the screen.
....

d Put the document into the machine ... then dial the number and press the button which ...
....

e Click on the item you want ... then you have to give your address and credit card details ...
....

f ... if you can't find the information you want, click on *Links* and you'll see a list of other websites.
....

g Press the green button, and you'll hear a tone ... then dial the phone number. Don't forget the code.
....

h Don't forget to write your name inside! Then put it in an envelope, write the address and post it.
....

Vocabulary booster: the post

postcard	birthday cards	post box	parcel
envelope	invitation	stamps	note	postman
posting a letter			

10 **a)** Match a word from the box to the correct picture.

1 *postcard*.............
2 ....
3 ....
4 ....
5 ....
6 ....
7 ....
8 ....
9 ....
10 ....

b) Listen to the pronunciation of the words on the recording. Practise saying them.

Pronunciation

Past participles

11 **a)** Look at the list of past participles below. Underline the sound which has a different pronunciation.

1	sent	met	made	said	read
2	done	gone	run	won	begun
3	made	played	stayed	paid	fed
4	stolen	spoken	told	got	chosen
5	caught	bought	drawn	shown	taught

b) Listen to the pronunciation of the words on the recording. Practise saying them.

Improve your writing

Writing a note

12 **a)** Read the note on the right and answer these questions.

1 Who is it for? *Joe*..................
2 Who wrote it? ....
3 Where did she go? ....
4 When will she be back? ....

Hi Joe,
Hope you had a good day at work!
Gone to supermarket to get something for dinner. Back at 6.
See you then.
Love,
Fiona

LOOK!

When we write a note, we often miss out words like:

articles	~~the~~ *supermarket*
pronouns and auxiliary verbs	~~I~~ *hope ...* ~~I've~~ *gone*
and we use shorter forms	*6 = 6 o'clock* *Hi!* *Thanks = Thank you*

b) Tom is on holiday. Charlotte is looking after his cats. Cross out or change the underlined words to make Tom's note for Charlotte.

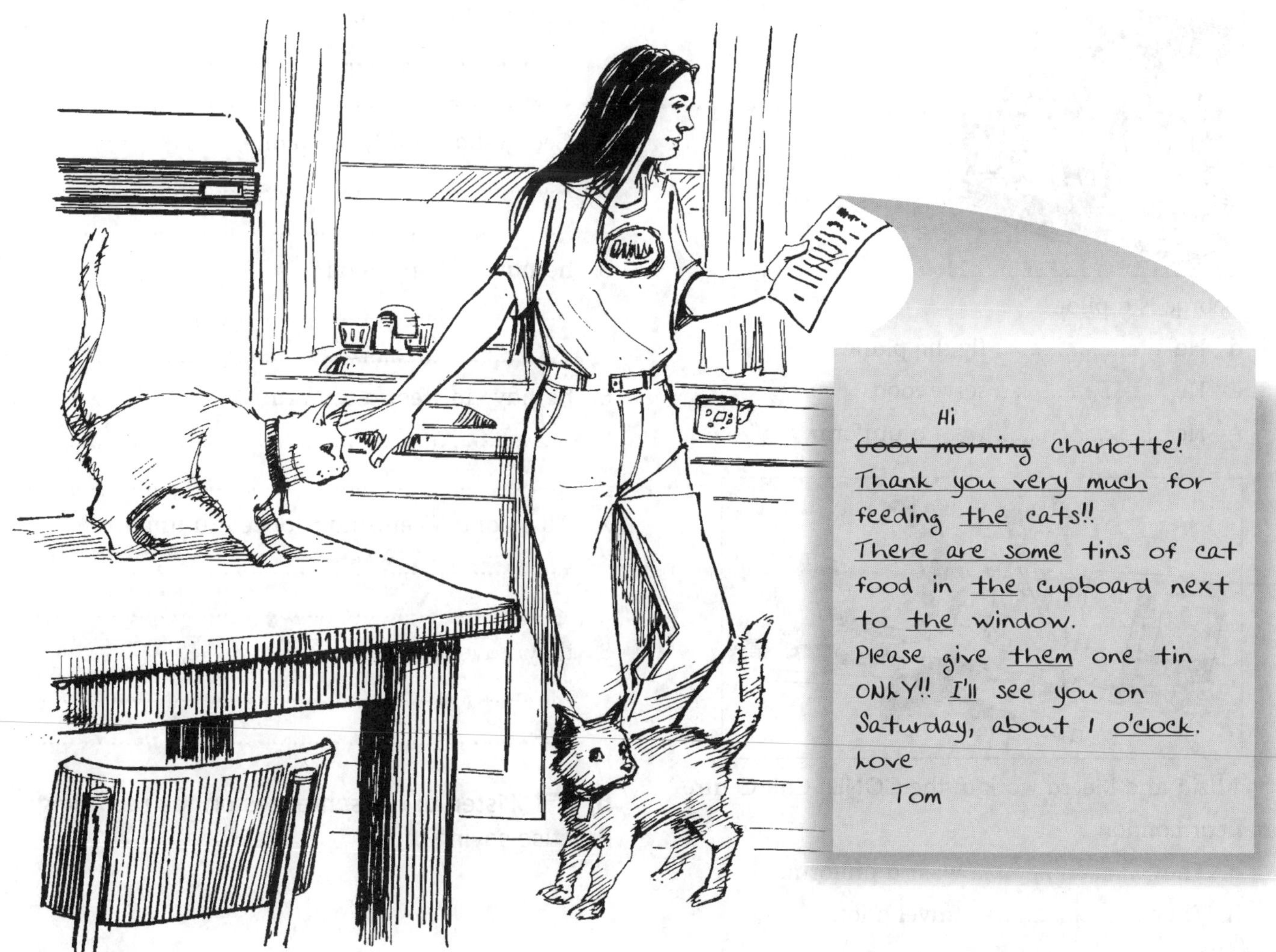

Hi
~~Good morning~~ Charlotte!
<u>Thank you very much</u> for feeding <u>the</u> cats!!
<u>There are some</u> tins of cat food in <u>the</u> cupboard next to <u>the</u> window.
Please give <u>them</u> one tin ONLY!! <u>I'll</u> see you on Saturday, about 1 <u>o'clock</u>.
Love
Tom

module 14

have to, don't have to

1 Bruce, George, Alizia and Meera all work for GONE!! airline. Complete the sentences about them with *has/have to* or *doesn't/don't have to*.

Bruce is a member of the cabin crew.

a He *has to*............... look after passengers.

b He .... use a computer.

c He .... look smart.

George is a pilot.

d He .... fly the plane.

e He .... serve food.

f He .... wear a uniform.

Alizia and Meera work at the GONE!! Call Centre near London.

g They .... wear a uniform.

h They .... travel a lot.

Questions and short answers

2 **a)** Write questions as in the example, and give the correct short answer.

> LOOK!
>
> **Short answers with *have to***
>
> **Do** I/you/we/they **have to** go?
> **Yes**, I/you/we/they **do**.
> **No**, I/you/we/they **don't**.
>
> **Does** he/she/it **have to** go?
> **Yes**, he/she/it **does**.
> **No**, he/she/it **doesn't**.

1 Bruce/have to/look after the passengers?
Does Bruce have to look after the passengers?
Yes, he does.

2 he/have to/use a computer?
....
....

3 he/have to/look smart?
....
....

4 George/have to/fly the plane?
....
....

5 he/have to/serve food?
....
....

6 he/have to/wear a uniform?
....
....

7 Alizia and Meera/have to/wear a uniform?
....
....

8 they/have to/travel a lot?
....
....

b) Listen to the sentences on the recording. Practise saying them.

have to, don't have to, can, can't

3 **a)** Look at the information about flights to New York on two airlines – BAC and GONE!! airlines - and complete the sentences with *have to*, *don't have to*, *can* or *can't*.

	The British Airline Company	GONE!!
Ticket price	1st class return ticket: £1,500	Standby ticket: £150
Check-in time	1 hour before	be at the airport 3 hours before
Before the flight	special VIP lounge	wait in Departure Lounge only
Food and drink	yes – free	buy sandwiches and drinks on plane
In-flight film	yes	no
Seats	seat numbers	no seat numbers
duty-free goods	yes	no

On BAC airlines:

1 You *have to*.............. check in one hour before.
2 You .... wait in the VIP lounge.
3 You .... pay for your food and drinks.
4 You .... watch an in-flight film.
5 You .... sit in a particular seat.
6 You .... buy duty-free goods.

On GONE!! airlines:

7 You .... arrive at the airport three hours before.
8 You .... use the VIP lounge.
9 You .... pay for your food and drinks.
10 You .... watch an in-flight film.
11 You .... sit where you want.
12 You .... buy duty-free goods.

b) Listen to the sentences on the recording. Practise saying them.

Vocabulary

Town facilities

4 Here is a list of places that János wants to visit while he is in Branton. Use the words in the box to answer the questions.

> the park the art gallery
> the beach ~~the square~~
> the sports stadium
> the river the museum
> the shopping centre

Where can he:

a sit with a coffee and watch people walk past?
the square.........
b see paintings?
....
c watch an athletics meeting?
....
d go shopping?
....
e see interesting old objects and learn about history?
....
f sunbathe and go swimming?
....
g sit and relax in a place with grass and trees?
....
h go on a boat trip?
....

5

Which A is a place where aeroplanes take off and land?	A *IRPORT*
Which B goes across a road, railway line or a river?	B _ _ _ _ _
Which C is a large strong building?	C _ _ _ _ _
Which D is something you ask for when you're lost?	D _ _ _ _ _ _ _ _ _
Which E is the opposite of *beginning*	E _ _
Which F means *wonderful* or *great*?	F _ _ _ _ _ _ _ _
Which G is a place where you see paintings?	G _ _ _ _ _ _
Which H is a small mountain?	H _ _ _
Which I is the opposite of *boring*?	I _ _ _ _ _ _ _ _ _ _
Which J is a trip from one place to another?	J _ _ _ _ _ _
Which K is 1,000 metres?	K _ _ _ _ _ _ _ _
Which M is a very high place - the Matterhorn, for example?	M _ _ _ _ _ _ _
When something is N, it means that you have to do it.	N _ _ _ _ _ _ _ _
Which O is the opposite of *closed*?	O _ _ _
Which P is a place in a town with trees, grass, flowers etc.?	P _ _ _
Which R is the Thames, the Amazon and the Nile?	R _ _ _ _
Which S is a stone model of a famous person?	S _ _ _ _ _
Which T is something you have to buy when you travel by bus/train etc.?	T _ _ _ _ _
Which U is the opposite of *over*?	U _ _ _ _
Which W is a way to get from one place to another using your legs?	W _ _ _

Prepositions of movement

6 Underline the correct preposition in each sentence.

a Walk *along/into/out of* the main street until you come to the main square.

b If you want to get to the main shopping area, go *into/over/through* the river to the north of the city.

c It's a long walk *from/out of/up* the hill, but at the end of it you can see the whole city ... it's wonderful!

d There's a bus stop near the school where you can get a bus *down/over/to* the town centre.

e The Number Six tram goes *across/past/through* the door of our apartment.

f You can now fly *across/along/past* the Atlantic Ocean in less than six hours.

g How long does it take to drive *down/from/to* here to the coast?

h Most visitors park their cars outside and then walk *along/into/over* the centre.

Listen and read

Unusual places to visit

7 Read and listen to the text about three unusual places to visit, and complete the table below.

	Blue Lagoon	London Bridge	Guggenheim Museums
What it is			
Where it is	45 km from Reykjavik, Iceland		
Why people go there			

Blue Lagoon - Iceland

Iceland - a country in the North Atlantic near the Arctic Circle - probably isn't the first place you think of for a perfect beach holiday. But every year, thousands of people take off their clothes and swim at the Blue Lagoon, a beach near the Arctic Circle and just 45 km from the capital city, Reykjavik. The air temperature can be as low as –10 degrees: but the water comes from underground and is naturally hot - the usual water temperature is between 35 and 40 degrees. It's like taking a hot bath in the open air!!

London Bridge - USA!!

The original London Bridge actually isn't in London at all ... and it doesn't even pass over a river!! American businessman Robert P McCulloch bought the bridge for $2.5 million in 1968 and moved it - stone by stone - across the Atlantic Ocean. He rebuilt it in Lake Havasu City, Arizona - a small town in the middle of the desert, where the temperature is often more than 40 degrees. Nowadays, thousands of tourists come to see the bridge, and there is an English village with watersports facilities, shops and restaurants.

The Guggenheim Museums

There are not one but five Guggenheim Museums. Solomon R Guggenheim opened the first collection of modern art in New York in 1959. Another museum opened in Italy, and then, in 1997, two more Guggenheims opened: one in Berlin and the other in the Basque city of Bilbao, in the north-west of Spain. It is now one of Spain's biggest tourist attractions, and every year hundreds of thousands of people come to see the paintings and other works of art. The newest Guggenheim museum is the Virtual Museum - the world's biggest Internet art gallery.

Vocabulary booster: a shopping centre

an escalator a push chair steps shoppers
a clothes shop a department store
a shop window automatic doors ~~a lift~~ a bench

8 **a)** Label the objects in the picture with words from the box.

2 ....
3 ....
4 ....
5 ....
6 ....
7 ....
8 ....
9 ....
10 ....

b) Listen to the pronunciation of the words on the recording. Practise saying them.

Spelling and pronunciation

Silent letters

9 **a)** All the words in the box have at least one silent letter. Which letter(s) don't we pronounce? Cross out the silent letters, as in the example.

1 cas~~t~~le	3 scenery	5 building	7 design	9 sights	11 sign
2 straight	4 highest	6 through	8 know	10 right	12 listen

b) Listen to the pronunciation of the words on the recording. Practise saying them.

Improve your writing

A postcard

10 **a)** James and Thelma are spending a few days in London. They have written a postcard to their neighbours in the United States. Read the postcard and write the words from the box into the correct space.

~~Hi~~	nearest	have	great	
English	seen	Bye	tea	in

(1) ...*Hi*.... everybody!!
Here we are (2) .... London!
The weather isn't too bad and we're having a (3) .... time. We've (4) .... the Changing of the Guard at Buckingham Palace, and right now we're having a cup of (5) ....
The kids want to go to the (6) .... McDonald's, but Thelma and I want to (7) .... lunch in a real old (8) .... pub near Westminster Abbey.
(9) .... for now!
Bob, Thelma and the kids

The Watts Family
5831 Hills Avenue
Daytoun,
Virginia VA 838
USA

b) Choose a place and write a postcard to someone you know. Use some of the phrases below.

Useful language

Here we are in ...	We've seen ...	The weather is(n't) ...
Right now, we're ...	We want to ...	We're having a ...time
We're going to ...	... want(s) to go to ...	Bye for now!

module 15

Infinitive of purpose

1 Last Friday, Carol went into town. Why did she visit these places? Write sentences with the infinitive of purpose, using the phrases in the box.

borrow some books have lunch buy some meat ~~get some money~~ buy some fruit catch the bus home visit her sick friend send a parcel to her cousin

a the bank
She went to the bank to get some money.

b the library
....

c the post office
....

d the hospital
....

e the greengrocer's
....

f the butcher's
....

g *The Oak Tree Café*
....

h the bus station
....

might, might not

2 **a)** Rewrite the sentences using *might* or *might not* instead of the words in **bold**.

1 **Perhaps** we'll go swimming this afternoon.
We *might go swimming this afternoon.*

2 **It's possible that** the plane **will** arrive late.
The plane ....

3 **Maybe** you'll be rich one day, if you work hard.
You ....

4 **It's possible that** I **won't** be able to come to class next week.
I ....

5 I **possibly won't** see Frank this weekend.
I ....

6 **Perhaps** Philip **won't** stay until the end of the course.
Philip ....

7 The government **will possibly** change the education system soon.
The government ....

8 **Maybe** the exam **won't** be as difficult as you think.
The exam ....

b) Listen to the sentences on the recording. Practise saying them.

will and *won't* (*probably*)

3 a) Rearrange the words to make sentences.

1 probably – another – be – It – tomorrow – will – nice day
It will probably be another nice day tomorrow.

2 time – won't – There – to stop for lunch – be – probably
....
....

3 be – will – class – probably – for – late – Martha
....
....

4 need – your – You – probably – umbrella – won't
....
....

5 be able – tomorrow – I – to come – won't – probably
....
....

6 soon – There – probably – be – an election – will
....
....

b) Listen to the sentences on the recording. Practise saying them.

might (not), *will* and *won't*

4 a) Tom, Meg, and Sampath are three school friends who have just finished their exams. Read the notes about their plans for the future.

	Holiday?	University?	Job?
Tom	no plans – Greece maybe	maybe not!	my father's company, probably
Meg	probably Spain with my parents	next year, probably	all my family are doctors, so why not me?
Sampath	don't think I'll have time	not sure – perhaps get a job abroad instead	who knows – an actor?

b) Use the information to write sentences with *might*, *might not*, *will probably* or *probably won't*.

1 Tom *might go to Greece for his holiday*. (*go to Greece*)
2 Meg .... (*go to Spain*)
3 Sampath .... (*have time for a holiday*)
4 Tom .... (*go to university*)
5 Meg .... (*go to university next year*)
6 Sampath .... (*get a job abroad instead*)
7 Tom .... (*work for his father's company*)
8 Meg .... (*become a doctor*)
9 Sampath .... (*become an actor*)

Infinitives with and without *to*

5 Underline the correct form in the sentences below.

a Taka wants *learn*/*to learn* more about computers.

b Paul is studying English *get*/*to get* a better job.

c It might *be*/*to be* better if you do it yourself.

d I'm going to the supermarket *buy*/*to buy* some bread. Do you want anything?

e Charles probably won't *pass*/*to pass* the exam.

f Thousands of people went to Australia *to watch*/*watch* the Olympics.

g We might not *have*/*to have* a holiday this year.

Vocabulary

Education and learning

6 Complete the text with words from the box.

subjects take secondary failed ~~primary~~ doing qualifications pass graduates at foreign

Is there really a big difference between boys and girls at school? New research says there is.

British girls between the ages of five and eleven have always done better at (a) *primary* school than boys: but now older girls are doing better at (b) .... school too.
Many people think that boys are better (c) .... science and mathematics and that girls do well in (d) .... languages and art. But more and more women are going to university, and (e) .... courses in (f) .... like law and engineering.
Every year, tens of thousands of British teenagers (g) .... their 'A' or Advanced level exams. These are the exams which young people need to (h) .... if they want to go to university. But in 2000, more boys than girls (i) .... their 'A' levels. Too many young boys leave school with no (j) .... at all. For young men like this, it is very difficult to find a good job these days, when big companies are looking for the best (k) ....

7 Look at the extracts from some children's textbooks. What subject are they about?

~~English~~ Mathematics Science Geography Information Technology History Art Music

(A) *English*

All these words start with *com* (Latin: *with*). See if you know the English meaning. Then check in your dictionary.
complete, compare,

(B) ____________

São Paulo, Brazil, is South America's largest city and one of the fastest-growing cities in the world. It is the commercial centre of

(C) ____________

The memory of a computer consists of microchips. There are two types: ROM (read-only memory) contains permanent instructions,

(D) ____________

In the fourteenth century, Arab traders sailed across the Indian Ocean and introduced Islam to many Asian countries. In 1511,

(E) ____________

How to draw a cat
Start by drawing a circle, like this:

(F) ____________

These symbols tell the musician how long to play each note. This

(G) ____________

H_20 - This chemical symbol for water means that each water molecule contains two atoms of hydrogen and one atom of

(H) ____________

875 ÷ 43 = 20.3488

Listen and read

8 Read and listen to the text about *The Five Ages of English*. Match the pictures with the paragraphs.

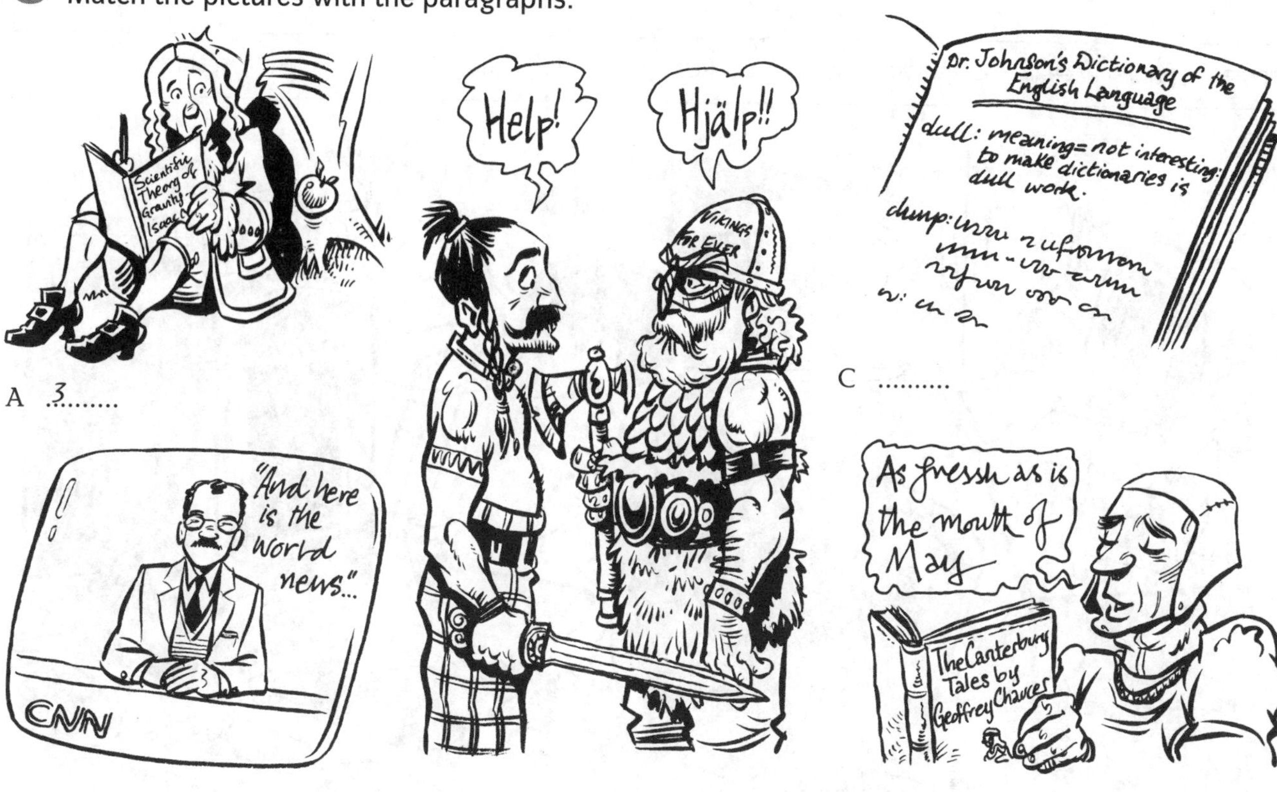

A 3.........

C ....

D ....

B ....

E ....

The Five Ages of English

1 Old English

From about the ninth century, the Vikings - who lived in what is now Sweden and Norway, began to arrive in the north of England. The language people spoke began to change. In the south of England, people began to translate books from Latin into English.

2 Middle English

In 1066, the Normans invaded England and French became the official language. Most educated people had to speak three languages: French, Latin and English! At this time, English literature began to develop. One of the most famous writers was the poet Geoffrey Chaucer in the fourteenth century. His language is a little like the English of today.

3 Early Modern English

(1450-1750)

This period includes the time of William Shakespeare - England's greatest writer. By the end of the seventeenth century, great scientists, like Isaac Newton, wrote in English, not in Latin. The British Empire began, and the English language travelled across the Atlantic to North America, and across Asia to India.

4 Modern English

(1750-1950)

English was now a national language. The first dictionary - Johnson's Dictionary - appeared in 1755, and the first grammar books appeared soon after.

As the British Empire grew in the nineteenth century, English became a more international language. People began to learn English around the world. The first English language textbooks appeared in the 1930s.

5 Late Modern English

(from 1950)

Now, English language teaching is an important international industry. After World War II, the United States became the most important economic and cultural power in the world, and a world market in audio-visual communication began. CNN International began in 1989 and the Internet developed in the 1990s. English became a global language, with about two billion speakers.

Vocabulary booster: in an Internet café

9 **a)** Label the objects in the picture with words from the box.

screen printer ~~chair~~ keyboard mouse CD-ROM drive document desk modem scanner

1 *chair* .... 3 .... 5 .... 7 .... 9 ....
2 .... 4 .... 6 .... 8 .... 10 ....

b) Listen to the pronunciation of the words on the recording. Practise saying them.

c) Write the words in one of the categories below.

Part of a computer	Connected to the computer	Not connected to the computer
screen	....	....
....	....	....
....	....	....
....	....	....

Pronunciation

Contracted forms

10 **a)** Listen to the sounds and the example words below.

/ɑː/	art	father	car
/əʊ/	know	go	home
/ɜː/	work	girl	birth

b) Notice the same sounds in these contracted forms.

/ɑː/	aren't	can't
/əʊ/	don't	won't
/ɜː/	weren't	

Improve your writing

Abbreviations on application forms (*Mr*, *Mrs*, *Dr*, *n/a*)

11 **a)** Write the abbreviations for these words.

Mister	*Mr*......	January	....	October	....
Doctor	....	not applicable	....	December	....
Number	....	September	....	*et cetera* (= and the others)	....

b) Here are some other abbreviations you see on application forms. Match the words on the right to the correct abbreviations.

1	Ave	Street
2	e.g.	Avenue
3	kg	kilometres
4	km	North, South, East, West
5	Mon/Tues/Wed/Thurs	*exempli gratia* (= for example)
6	N/S/E/W	Park
7	Pk	Road
8	Rd	kilograms
9	St	United States of America
10	tel	United Kingdom
11	UK	telephone
12	USA	Monday, Tuesday, Wednesday, Thursday

c) Rewrite the following with abbreviations.

1 Mister James Hewson
Mr James Hewson..
....

2 2 kilograms
....
....

3 63 Stamford Street
....
....

4 irregular verbs, for example *bring* and *buy*
....
....

5 Queen's Park Road
....
....

6 London South-West 7
....
....

7 10 kilometres
....
....

8 arrived in the United Kingdom from the United States
....
....

9 telephone number: 020 7939 3671
....
....

10 classes are on Tuesday and Thursday
....
....

11 January–March and April–September
....
....

Pronunciation table

Consonants		Vowels	
Symbol	**Key Word**	**Symbol**	**Key Word**
p	**p**et	iː	sl**ee**p
b	**b**oat	ɪ	b**i**t
t	**t**op	e	b**e**t
d	**d**o	æ	b**a**t
k	**c**at	ɑː	c**ar**
g	**g**olf	ɒk	cl**o**ck
tʃ	**ch**ur**ch**	ɔː	b**ough**t
dʒ	**j**eans	ʊː	b**oo**k
f	**f**ew	uː	b**oo**t
v	**v**iew	ʌ	b**u**t
θ	**th**irsty	ɜː	b**ir**d
ð	**th**ough	ə	broth**er**
s	**s**it	eɪ	d**ay**
z	**z**oo	əʊ	ph**o**ne
ʃ	fre**sh**	aɪ	b**y**
ʒ	lei**s**ure	aʊ	n**ow**
h	**h**at	ɔɪ	b**oy**
m	**m**other	ɪə	d**ea**r
n	su**n**	ɛə	h**ai**r
ŋ	you**ng**	ʊə	d**oor**
l	**l**ot	ɪ	happ**y**
r	**r**un	ʊ	ann**u**al
j	**y**es		
w	**w**et		

Answer key

module 1

Names and countries

1 a)

2 's
3 What
4 your
5 name
6 Nice
7 you
8 And
9 this
10 Hello

Personal information: *be*

2 b)

1 's her name?
2 name's Gisele Bundchen.
3 's she from?
4 's from Brazil.

c)

1 are their names?
2 names are Andrea, Caroline and Sharon Corr.
3 are they from?
4 're from Ireland.

d)

1 What's her name?
2 Her name's Venus Williams.
3 Where's she from?
4 She's from the USA.

e)

1 What are their names?
2 Their names are David and Victoria Beckham.
3 Where are they from?
4 They're from England.

f)

1 What's his name?
2 His name's Roberto Benigni.
3 Where's he from?
4 He's from Italy.

is or *are*

3

b are, c Is, d is, e Are, f Are, g is

Negative sentences

4

b I'm not from Ireland.
c My mother and father aren't English.
d Brazil isn't a small country.
e My name isn't Lana.
f My sister isn't married.
g I'm not 15 years old.
h Philip and Elizabeth aren't on holiday.

Personal questions: *be*

5 a)

2 you
3 brothers
4 student
5 English
6 Michelle
7 from
8 holiday

Short answers

6

b he is
c it isn't
d we aren't/we're not
e she is
f I am
g he isn't
h they aren't
i it is
j she isn't

Possessive adjectives

7

b my, c Her, d our, e our, f their, g her, h his, i our, j your, k My

Indefinite article: *a(n)*

8

b a, c an, d a, e a, f a, g a, h an

Vocabulary

Jobs

9

b waiter
c police officer
d musician
e teacher
f sportsman
g artist
h doctor

Vocabulary booster: countries and nationalities

10 a)

2 Brazilian
3 Italian
4 English
5 Spanish
6 Scottish
7 French
8 American

Listen and read

11

b Donna Fiorelli
c Béatrice Santini
d Plankton
e Magnus Mills
f Betty Booth
g Magnus Mills
h Donna Fiorelli

Punctuation: capital letters

12

b **M**y mother's from the **U**nited **S**tates.
c **A**re you **S**panish?
d **O**ur school is in **C**amden **R**oad.
e **I**'m from **R**ome.
f **E**ric lives in **B**erlin.

Improve your writing
Addresses in English

13 b)

1 South London College
52, Richmond Road
London
SW15 6GS
UK

2 Mrs Mary Burke
109 St Stephen Street
Dublin
4
Ireland

c)
Miss Sarah Ellis
62 High Street
Amersham
HP7 ODJ
England

Mr Simon Henderson
12 Muirfield Road
Glasgow
G12 8SJ
Scotland

Pronunciation
/ ɒ /, / eɪ / and / aɪ /

14 b)

2 / eɪ /
3 / ɒ /
4 / ɒ /
5 / aɪ /
6 / eɪ /
7 / aɪ /
8 / ɒ /

module 2

Identifying objects: *this*, *that*, *these*, *those*

1

b those
c that
d this
e these
f those
g these
h that

a/an or ø with objects and plurals

2

b an, c an, d a, e an, f ø, g a, h ø, i a, j an

have/has got

3

2 's got, 3 hasn't got, 4 haven't got, 5 've got, 6 've got, 7 's got, 8 hasn't got, 9 's got

Questions and short answers

4 a)

2 Has she got a car?
Yes, she has.
3 Has she got a computer?
No, she hasn't.
4 Have Martin and Inge got a pet?
No, they haven't.
5 Have they got a car?
Yes, they have.
6 Have they got a computer?
Yes, they have.
7 Has Alfonso got a pet?
Yes, he has.
8 Has he got a car?
No, he hasn't.
9 Has he got a computer?
Yes, he has.

's = is or *has?*

5 a)

My friend Steve**'s** got a fantastic life, he**'s** only 21, but he**'s** got a great job – he**'s** a professional footballer – and he**'s** got lots of money. He**'s** got a new car, too – it**'s** a Porsche. It**'s** white, and it**'s** got everything, even a CD player!

b)

2 is
3 has
4 is
5 has
6 has
7 is
8 is
9 has

Adjectives and nouns

6

b Your dog has got **beautiful** eyes.
c We've got two **black** cats at home.
d I've got a **fantastic** computer game – *Crash 5!!!*
e My friend Al is a **professional** musician.
f Lauren Bacall is my **favourite** actress.
g My sister's got a **new** mobile phone.
h Goldie is a **friendly** dog.

Vocabulary booster: more everyday objects

7 a)

1 a mirror
2 a hairbrush
3 tube of lipstick
4 a pen
5 a calculator
6 car keys
7 a packet of chewing gum
8 a passport
9 an address book
10 a pencil

Vocabulary
Relationship vocabulary

8 b)

2 son
3 mother
4 father
5 parents
6 husband

c)
(*possible answers*)
2 He's Joe and Brenda's son. He's Nora's grandson. He's Jane's brother.
3 He's Brenda's husband. He's Jane and Jason's father.
4 She's Joe's wife. She's Nora's daughter. She's Jane and Jason's mother.
5 She's Joe and Brenda's daughter. She's Nora's granddaughter. She's Colin's wife. She's Jason's sister.
6 They're Joe and Brenda's children. They're Nora's grandchildren.

Listen and read

9 b)

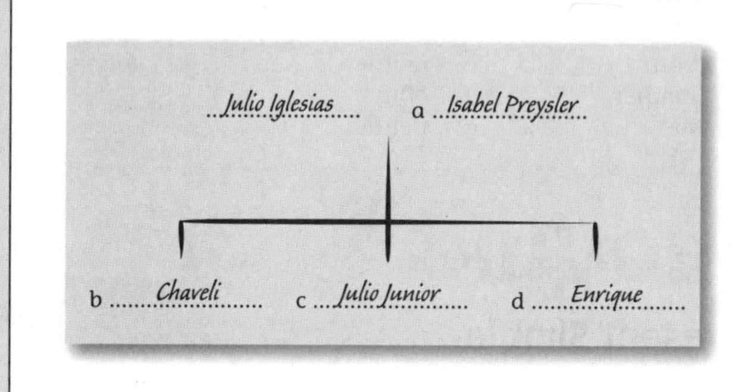

Possessive 's

10

b Is that Michael**'s** car?
c It's Tessa**'s** birthday on Saturday.
d What's your mother**'s** name?
e Where's Philip**'s** desk?
f My husband**'s** name is Peter.
g Jo is my sister**'s** friend.
h Carla**'s** house is in the centre of Rome.

Spelling

Plurals

11 a)

2	dictionaries	6	keys	10	buses
3	boxes	7	matches	11	addresses
4	universities	8	watches	12	boys
5	babies	9	houses		

b)

2	wives	4	men	6	lives
3	feet	5	women		

Pronunciation

The sounds / s / and / z /

12 a)

What's this?
It's my passport.

b)
His friend's name is James.

c/d)
1 This is my sister. Her name's Suzanne.
2 Those are my keys!
3 She's seven years old.
4 What's his address?
5 She's got fantastic blue eyes.
6 What's your brother's first name?
7 Sarah is a famous actress.
8 What's the answer to this question?

Prepositions

13

a	in	c	in	e	at
b	with	d	at	f	in

module 3

Present Simple

Questions

1 a)

2	Do	5	French	8	like
3	football	6	study		
4	you	7	in		

Negatives

2 a)

2 Cats don't like water.
3 Most people don't go to work on Sunday.
4 Babies don't go to school.
5 Banks in Britain don't close at lunchtime.
6 Most restaurants don't open in the morning.
7 My grandparents don't like rock music.

Positive and negative

3 b)

2	live	7	drink	13	like
3	speak	8	don't drink	14	don't like
4	don't speak	10	don't live	15	don't drink
5	like	11	speak	16	drink
6	don't like	12	don't speak		

Questions and short answers

4

b Yes, they do.
c No, they don't.
d No, they don't.
e Yes, they do.
f No, they don't.
g No, they don't.
h No, they don't.

Subject and object pronouns

5

b her, c us, d me, e it, f him, g them, h it/me

Vocabulary
Collocations with common verbs

6

b milk, tea, mineral water
c in a flat, in a house, in a city
d a meal, a snack, breakfast
e to school, to university, home
f law, economics, English grammar

Vocabulary booster: buildings

7 a)

1 a block of flats
2 a school
3 a hospital
4 a bank
5 a hotel
6 a supermarket
7 a railway station
8 a library

Listen and read

8 b)

2 They open at seven o'clock.
3 They have lunch at school.
4 They finish at six o'clock.
5 They go to the library.
6 They close at eleven or twelve o'clock.
7 They go home in a special minibus.
8 They go to bed at one or two o'clock.

Prepositions: *in*, *at* or *to*

9

b in/in
c to/at
d in
e in
f at
g to
h in
i at
j at/in

Opposites

10

b evening
c get up
d close
e come home from work

Pronunciation
The letter *i*

11 b)

/ɪ/ drink, six, big, finish, this, children, listen, dinner
/aɪ/ life, nine, time, five, write, night

Improve your writing
Commas, full stops, *and* and *but*

12 a)

In Britain, children start school at about 9 o'clock in the morning, but in Poland, they start school at 8 o'clock.

b)

3 In New York, most people start work at 8 a.m., but in York, most people start work at 9 a.m.
4 In York, most people start work at 9 a.m. and they finish work at 5.30 p.m.
5 In New York most people finish work at 6 p.m., but in York, they finish work at 5.30 p.m.
6 In New York, children start school at 5 years, but in York, they start school at 4 years.
7 In New York, most shops open at 9 a.m. and they close at 8 p.m.
8 In New York, most shops close at 8 p.m., but in York, they close at 6 p.m.

too, *both* and *neither*

13

b both
c neither
d too
e neither
f both
g neither
h too

module 4

Present Simple
Spelling

1

b watch**es**
c come**s**
d live**s**
e go**es**
f enjoy**s**
g say**s**
h stud**ies**
i play**s**

Present Simple with *he/she/it*

2 a)

2 studies
3 lives
4 speaks
5 likes

c)

2 He comes from Britain.
3 He lives in Seoul/South Korea.
4 He speaks English, French and Korean.
5 He plays the guitar.
7 She comes from Argentina.
8 She speaks Spanish, Catalan and English.
9 She works in a bank.
10 She goes to the gym.
12 He comes from Hungary.
13 He lives in Paris/France.
14 He teaches music.
15 He plays tennis.

Short answers

3 a)

3 No, she doesn't.
4 Yes, she does.
5 Yes, she does.
6 No, he doesn't.
7 Yes, he does.
8 Yes, he does.
9 No, he doesn't.
10 No, he doesn't.

Negatives

4 a)

2 It doesn't rain in summer.
3 My brother doesn't like getting up at seven o'clock.
4 The restaurant doesn't close on Sunday evening.
5 Martin doesn't come to class every week.
6 Tony doesn't buy all his food at the supermarket.
7 Carla doesn't drive to work.
8 My cousin doesn't visit me every month.

Positives and negatives

5

b leaves
c writes
d lives
e gets up
f has
g drives
h reads
i buys
j sells
k finishes
l says
m doesn't work
n works

Questions

6

b When does he get up?
c What does he do after breakfast?
d Where does he read the newspaper?
e Where does he go on holiday?
f What does he do after lunch?
g What time does he finish work?

Adverbs of frequency

7

b sometimes
c usually
d never
e often
f always
g never
h always

Activity verbs

8

b go/go
c watch
d listen/listen
e plays
f write/write
g visit
h study

Word order: frequency adverbs, auxiliaries

9

b Caroline never eats fish.
c I don't often eat in a restaurant.
d I usually get up late on a Sunday morning.
e It's always very hot in August in my city.
f The Brown family usually goes to Italy on holiday.
g The weather is always cold in January.
h The bus is often late.

Vocabulary booster: everyday activities

10 a)

1 go for a run
2 go to the gym
3 cook a meal
4 clean your teeth
5 wake up
6 go for a walk
7 meet friends
8 have a shower
9 catch a bus
10 get dressed

c)

In the morning	**In the afternoon/evening**
clean your teeth	clean your teeth
go for a run	go for a run
have a shower	catch a bus
get dressed	go to the gym
wake up	cook a meal
catch a bus	meet friends

like, love, hate + -ing

11 b)

2 Irene hates doing housework.
Agnes loves doing housework.
3 Irene loves talking to the family.
Agnes doesn't like talking to the family.
4 Irene likes going to English class.
Agnes hates going to English class.
5 Irene doesn't like babysitting.
Agnes likes babysitting.

Listen and read

12 b)

2 In the south of France, or in Tuscany, in the north of Italy.
3 Paris.
4 London.
5 In a small house in Gascony.
6 In France.
7 Four.
8 The weather, the food and wine and the people.
9 They come from England.

Pronunciation

Plural nouns with /s/, /z/ and /ɪz/

13 b)

2 crowds /z/
3 spiders /z/
4 actresses /ɪz/
5 beaches /ɪz/
6 drivers /z/
7 students /s/
8 restaurants /s/
9 houses /ɪz/
10 friends /z/
11 parents /s/
12 addresses /ɪz/

Improve your writing

A paragraph about a friend

14 a)

2 G, 3 F, 4 A, 5 B, 6 H, 7 E, 8 D

b)

My friend Takashi **comes from** Okinawa in Japan, but now he **lives** in London.
He's a musician, and **he plays** in a bar called *East and West*. He **likes** the international atmosphere in London, but **he doesn't like** the rain! He **thinks** the people are very nice when you know them.

module 5

can/can't

1

b	can	e	can't	h	can't
c	can't	f	can	i	can't
d	can't	g	can		

Short answers

2 a)

1	Yes, you can.	4	Yes, you can.	7	Yes, you can.
2	Yes, you can.	5	No, they can't.	8	No, it can't.
3	No, you can't.	6	Yes, you can.	9	Yes, you can.

Articles: *a* and *the*

3

c I always drive to work, but **a** lot of people come by underground.
d Parking is **a** real problem near my house.
e The traffic is very bad in **the** evening.
f My uncle is **a** train driver.
g Have you got **a** car?
h We live in **a** small town in **the** United States.

4

b 8 o'clock is a good time to phone Thomas: he is always at ~~the~~ home in the evening.
c It's so cold today that a lot of people can't go to ~~the~~ work.
d The train times are different on ~~the~~ Sundays.
e What do you think of the public transport in ~~the~~ London?
f You can use a Rail Card in most countries in ~~the~~ Europe.
g Do ~~the~~ people drive on the left in the United States?
h Our plane arrives in Los Angeles at ~~the~~ 2 o'clock in the afternoon.

most, a lot of, some, not many

5

b Not many people work on Sundays.
c A lot of British people go to Spain on holiday.
d Some people can't drink coffee without sugar.
e A lot of people don't like flying.
f Not many European people can understand Japanese.
g Most people in my town enjoy talking to tourists.
h Some people drive dangerously at night.

Listen and read

6 b)

2 Moscow.
3 567.
4 The United States.
5 Forty-three million.
6 Mexico City.
7 Grand Central Terminal Station, New York.
8 Six hours.

Prepositions

7

b on, c to, d on, e to, f for, g off/on, h to/by, i from, j to

Vocabulary

Means of transport

8

b	motorbike	g	tram
c	scooter	h	train
d	bicycle	i	underground
e	car	j	taxi
f	aeroplane		

Vocabulary booster: travel

9 a)

1	a platform	6	a bus stop
2	a ticket machine	7	a parking meter
3	a railway bridge	8	a pavement
4	a car park	9	a pedestrian crossing
5	a motorway	10	a traffic light

Pronunciation

The letter *a*

10 b)

/ aː /	/ eɪ /	/ ɔː /	/ ae /
artist	make	walk	catch
can't	take	small	taxi
far	train	talk	traffic jam
car	wait	football	travel

Spelling

11

Everybody knows that the trafic (traffic) in our city is really bad, and there are always traffic jams in the morning and evning (evening). I haven't got a car, so like most people, I usually travell (travel) by bus. My jorney (journey) home takes more than an hour. Also, the bus is very croded (crowded) and sometimes I have to wait a long time for a bus wich (which) isn't full. If I rid (ride) my bicicle (bicycle), it only takes therty (thirty) minutes ... but it isn't easy bicause (because) of all the cars on the rode (road).

Improve your writing

Completing an immigration form

12

VISA WAIVER Immigration

Type or print legibly with pen in ALL CAPITAL LETTERS. **USE ENGLISH**.

1. Family name
PRESTON
2. First (given) name
ROBERT
3. Birth Date (*day / mo / yr*)
1120281
4. Country of Citizenship
UK
5. Sex (*male or female*)
MALE
6. Passport Number
7379355G
7. Airline and Flight Number
AA92951
8. Country where you live
UK
9. City where you boarded
LIMA

CERTIFICATION: I certify that I have read and understand all the questions and statements on this form. The answers I have furnished are true and correct to the best of my knowledge and belief.

Robert Preston — Signature

15.10.01 — Date

module 6

Countable and uncountable nouns

1 **a)**

Uncountable nouns: fruit, meat, water, tea, cheese, music, bread, food, sugar

b)

2 is
3 isn't/meals
4 takes
5 this/It's
6 are
7 too many
8 isn't

Vocabulary

Food

2

Drinks: mineral water, fruit juice, coffee, milk, tea.
Types of fruit: banana, apple, orange, grapes
Other things you can eat: cheese, ham, jam, yoghurt, eggs, toast, bread, butter, nuts, pizza, sausages, cereal.

there is/there are

3

b are there
c There's
d Are there
e Is there
f there aren't
g There are
h There isn't
i Is there
j There are

Short answers

4 **b)**

2 Are/Yes, there are.
3 Is/No, there isn't.
4 Is/Yes, there is.
5 Is/No, there isn't.
6 Is
7 Is/No, there isn't.
8 Are/No, there aren't.
9 Is/Yes, there is.
10 Are/Yes, there are.
11 Are/Yes, there are.

some and *any*

5 **a)**

2 some
3 some/any
4 any
5 some
6 some
7 any/some
8 any/some

some, *any*, *a(n)* and *no*

6 **a)**

2 no
3 a
4 some
5 An
6 any
7 no
8 some
9 A
10 some
11 a
12 a

Vocabulary booster: things to eat

7 **a)**

1 olives
2 oil
3 onions
4 rice
5 French fries
6 tomatoes
7 salad
8 potatoes
9 vinegar
10 crisps
11 salt
12 pepper

Listen and read

8

The correct picture is C.

Questions with *how much* and *how many*

9

b How much
c How much
d How many
e How much
f How much
g How many
h How many

Vocabulary

Containers: *a cup of*, *a glass of*, *a bottle of*

10 a)

2 a bag
3 a carton
4 a packet
5 a glass
6 a bottle

b)

2 packet
3 carton/bottle/glass
4 packet/bag
5 packet
6 bottle/glass
7 cup/packet
8 bottle/glass/cup
9 bottle/carton/glass
10 cup/packet

Pronunciation

Sentence stress

11 a)

1 Can I have a bottle of mineral water, please?
2 You can catch a bus to the airport from here.
3 How many packets of cigarettes do you buy in a week?
4 How much money have you got in your bag?
5 I always have orange juice with my breakfast.
6 How much water do you drink in a day?
7 What do you want for lunch?
8 I never drink coffee in the evening.

Improve your writing

Describing food from your country

12 a)

1 Italian
2 Japanese
3 French
4 Argentinian
5 Hungarian

module 7

Past Simple: *was/were*

1

b was/was
c were
d were
e was/were
f Was
g was
h was

Short answers

2 a)

3 Was/No, he wasn't.
4 Was/Yes, he was.
5 Were/No, they weren't.
6 Were/Yes, they were.
7 Was/Yes, she was.
8 Was/No, she wasn't.

Past Simple

Spelling of *-ed* endings

3

b enjoyed
c travelled
d studied
e looked
f danced
g played
h believed
i arrived
j tried
k received
l stayed

Regular verbs

4

b started/ended
c died
d walked
e helped
f studied
g tried
h changed
i lived

Irregular verbs

5

b left
c went
d began
e sang
f sold
g made
h won
i became

Regular and irregular verbs

6 a)

2 flew
3 started
4 arrived
5 wanted
6 met
7 became
8 loved
9 tried
10 gave
11 left
12 began
13 received
14 disappeared
15 spent
16 found

Past time phrases

7

b in the 19th century
c when they are 18
d when I was a child
e in 1990
f every week
g three years ago

Prepositions of time

8

b from/to
c at
d in
e At
f on
g In
h in

Pronunciation

Past tense endings

9 a)

3 S, 4 D, 5 D, 6 S, 7 S, 8 S, 9 S, 10 D

Vocabulary booster: common verbs

10 a)

1 throw
2 catch
3 wake up
4 break
5 fall
6 cut
7 steal
8 build
9 run
10 win

b)

2 catch
3 build
4 throw
5 wake up
6 run
7 steal
8 fall
9 cut
10 win

Listen and read

11 b)

A 3
B 1
C 4
D 5
E 2

Ordinal numbers

12

b fifth
c eighth
d nineteenth
e fourth
f twentieth
g first/second
h twenty-second

Improve your writing

Time linkers: *before*, *after*, *then*

13

b After
c before
d Then
e Then
f After
g Before
h before

module 8

Vocabulary

Common verbs in the past tense

1

b bought
c read
d slept
e saw
f drove
g wrote
h woke up
i wore
j found
k gave
l drank
m fell

Past Simple

Negative

2

b We didn't go for a drive yesterday.
c Ben didn't remember to buy a birthday card.
d I didn't hear the telephone.
e The letter didn't arrive this morning.
f I didn't eat in a restaurant last night.
g Amanda didn't know what to do.
h I didn't check my e-mail yesterday.

Questions

3

b Did Alexander Graham Bell invent e-mail?
c Did Marilyn Monroe sing *Candle in the Wind*?
d Did Captain Cook discover America?
e Did Leonardo da Vinci paint *Mona Lisa*?
f Did Madonna play *Evita*?
g Did Beethoven write rock songs?
h Did Laurel and Hardy make comedy films?
i Did Yuri Gagarin travel to the moon?

Short answers

4 a)

2 No, he didn't.
3 No, she didn't.
4 No, he didn't.
5 Yes, he did.
6 Yes, she did.
7 No, he didn't.
8 Yes, they did.
9 No, he didn't.

Question words

5 a)

2 How did he
3 Where did he
4 How much did it
5 What did he buy
6 How many books did he
7 How much money did he
8 What time/When did he
9 How long did the journey

Past Simple

Positive, negative and question forms

6

b saw (did)
c said (say)
d got (get)
e take (took)
f bought (buy)
g come (came)
h enjoyed (enjoy)
i understood (understand)
j went (go)

Prepositions

7

b up, c to, d in, e in, f out, g about, h by

Pronunciation

Past forms

8 b)

had, began, drank, ran, sang
read, fell, left, met
caught, bought, saw, thought, wore
cut, shut, won

Vocabulary booster: books, magazines and newspapers

9 a)

2 headline
3 front page
4 article
6 picture
7 pages
8 advertisement
10 title
11 author
12 cover

Listen and read

10 b)

2 What did Atatürk do in 1915?
3 When did he become the first President of the Republic of Turkey?
4 When did he die?
5 When did Florence Nightingale work in a hospital for wounded soldiers?
6 What did the soldiers call her?
7 When did she begin a school of nursing in London?

Improve your writing

A diary

11 a)

2 and listened to the music
3 only cost £50
4 we finally left London
5 When we arrived in France
6 was in another country
7 I didn't have any German money
8 I walked back to the car park
9 the bus wasn't there.

b)

3 sat
4 helped
5 spoke
6 told
7 said
8 got
9 drove
10 saw
11 opened
12 started
13 thought
14 remembered
15 stopped

module 9

Adjectives: opposites

1

b an easy question
c a small country
d an ugly face
e a new bicycle
f an uncomfortable chair
g a fast train

Comparative adjectives

2

b easier
c bigger
d cheaper
e healthier
f newer
g happier
h slimmer
i quieter
j hotter

3 a)

2 The River Mississippi is longer than the River Volga.
3 Blue whales are heavier than elephants.
4 The Pyramids are older than the Parthenon.
5 The Sears Tower is taller than the World Trade Center.
6 The Akashi-Kaikyo Bridge is longer than the Sydney Harbour Bridge.
7 Gold is more expensive than silver.
8 Esperanto is easier than English.

Superlative adjectives

4 b)

2 Karina Green is the youngest.
3 Karina Green has got the longest hair.
4 Jim Bowen has got the shortest hair.
5 Jim Bowen is the tallest.
6 Roy Seagrove is the heaviest.
7 Lilian Kay is the smallest.
8 Roy Seagrove is the most successful.

5

b smallest – Pluto
c biggest – Jupiter
d hottest – Venus
e furthest/coldest – Pluto
f easiest – Jupiter
g closest – Venus

Comparative and superlative adjectives

6 a)

2 the biggest
3 the best
4 larger
5 bigger
6 most delicious
7 bigger
8 more expensive
9 better

Vocabulary

Shops and shopping

7 a)

2 clothes shop
3 newsagent's
4 street market
5 bookshop
6 baker's
7 greengrocer's
8 post office
9 pharmacy
10 supermarket

Pronunciation

Comparatives

8 c)

1 Cats are bigger than tigers. ✗
2 Trains are faster than aeroplanes. ✗
3 Bicycles are slower than motorbikes. ✓
4 New York is older than Rome. ✗
5 Gold is more expensive than silver. ✓
6 Driving a car is more difficult than riding a bicycle. ✓

One and *ones*

9

b one is nearly three.
c the ones I bought.
d one, please.
e ones are the oldest.

Improve your writing

Describing a place

10 a)

2 it sells
3 The reason I like it is
4 is open
5 until eight o'clock at night
6 The best time to go is
7 The people there

Listen and read

11

b The Ultimate Power Control System
c The Freezolux Smart Fridge
d The Bryson D838 Robot Vacuum Cleaner
e The Ultimate Power Control System
f The Bryson D838 Robot Vacuum Cleaner

Vocabulary booster: a supermarket

12 a)

1 customer
2 plastic bags
3 till
4 cashier
5 checkout
6 cans
7 queue
8 shopping list
9 shopping trolley
10 shopping basket

module 10

Spelling

-ing forms

1

b	studying	f	stopping	j	giving
c	washing	g	looking	k	planning
d	leaving	h	dancing	l	driving
e	coming	i	staying		

Present Continuous

2 a)

2	is looking	5	is eating	8	are doing
3	is talking	6	is having		
4	is sitting	7	is watching		

Question words

3 a)

2 Where/To my English class.
3 Why/Because you look so funny!
4 Who/My brother.
5 What/Oh, nothing, just a magazine.
6 What/Ssh!! It's my favourite programme.

Short answers

4

b	No, it isn't.	f	Yes, he is.
c	Yes, they are.	g	No, she isn't.
d	Yes, we are.		
e	No, I'm not.		

All forms

5 a)

2	Are you enjoying	9	she isn't
3	I'm not	10	She isn't doing
4	I'm not having	11	She's looking
5	's happening	12	isn't listening
6	They're playing	13	's he doing
7	's dancing	14	's coming
8	Is she dancing		

Present Continuous and Present Simple

6

b	do you come	g	are you doing/I'm waiting
c	Do you speak	h	Are you reading
d	It's raining	i	We're having
e	I'm watching		
f	drive		

Vocabulary

Describing people

7

b 5, c 10, d 3, e 1, f 9, g 4, h 6, i 12, j 11, k 2, l 8

's

8 a)

2 Everybody says she'**s** very good-looking.
3 Where'**s** Frank going?
4 Who'**s** the girl with long dark hair?
5 Dina'**s** got short hair.
6 David'**s** mother doesn't wear glasses.
7 Ann'**s** the black girl with medium-length hair.
8 Maria'**s** waiting for me in the car.
9 My father'**s** got a moustache.
10 What colour are Barbara'**s** earrings?

b)

2 = is, 3 = is, 4 = is, 5 = has, 6 = possessive, 7 = is, 8 = is, 9 = has, 10 = possessive

Vocabulary

Clothes

9

b	Marie	e	Paul	h	Bob	k	Bob
c	Marie	f	Marie	i	Paul	l	Bob
d	Paul	g	Paul	j	Paul		

Listen and read

10

	Where is she from?	What clothes does she talk about?	Where did she buy her clothes?
Mina	London	jeans, jumper, jacket, shoes	*Michiko*, *Space*, Camden Market
Gloria	Barcelona, Spain	dress, trousers, shoes	She made them herself – she bought her shoes in Spain but she can't remember where from.
Alice	United States	top, trousers, shoes, jacket	Milan, New York

Improve your writing

Correcting mistakes

11

b	sitting	f	he's	j	she's
c	shining	g	has	k	look
d	are	h	isn't	l	attractive
e	wearing	i	eyes		

module 11

can/can't for ability

1 b)

3 She can't
4 She can
5 can speak French
6 can play chess
7 He can't drive a car.
8 He can't play a musical instrument.

Questions and short answers

2 a)

2 Can she play chess?
No, she can't.
3 Can she drive a car?
Yes, she can.
4 Can she play a musical instrument?
Yes, she can.
5 Can Max speak French?
No, he can't.
6 Can he play chess?
Yes, he can.
7 Can he drive a car?
Yes, he can.
8 Can he play a musical instrument?
No, he can't.

Question words

3

b What kind
c When
d Which
e What colour
f What time
g What
h How

4 b)

2 How fast can they run?
3 How many humps does a dromedary have?
4 How many camels are there in the world?
5 How tall is an adult camel?
6 How much does an adult camel weigh?
7 How far can camels walk without drinking?
8 How often do camels need to drink water?
9 How much water can they drink?

5

b How many
c Which
d How much
e Which
f How much
g How many
h How much
i What

Word order in questions

6

b How many films did he make?
c How long does a football match last?
d Where was the boxer Muhammad Ali born?
e How far is it from here to your home?
f What kind of music do you like?
g How fast can a cheetah run?
h What is the biggest ocean in the world?

Articles

7

b a, c an, d the, e the/the, f the, g the/the, h the, i a

Vocabulary booster: animals

8 a)

1 horse
2 dog
3 sheep
4 duck
5 cow
6 bees
7 monkey
8 spider
9 frog
10 mouse
11 beetle
12 snake

c)

Animals with two legs duck, monkey
Animals with four legs frog, cow, mouse, sheep, horse, dog
Animals with more than four legs bee, beetle, spider

Listen and read

9

b Up to 6 metres
c 6 cm
d 3 kg
e more than 2.5 metres
f 20–50 times a second
g more than 50
h i) 13 million ii) a few hundred iii) 50,000

More about numbers

10 a)

2 1985
3 3,000
4 90 km/h
5 9.6
6 253,000
7 62,000,000
8 297
9 2,000,000,000
10 963

b)

2 one hundred and fifty kilometres an hour
3 three million
4 eight point five
5 three hundred and forty-eight
6 two billion
7 five thousand six hundred
8 nineteen eighty
9 three hundred and fifty thousand
10 eighty million

Improve your writing

Full stops, apostrophes and question marks

12

b **I'm not sure what the answer is.**
c **Is it true that koala bears don't drink water?**
d **What is the world's largest animal?**
e **He doesn't know the answer.**
f **Where's the biggest lake in the world?**
g **What is Peter's pet dog's name?**

module 12

Future plans

going to

1 a)

2 He's going to buy a newspaper.
3 They're going to play tennis.
4 The bus is going to stop.
5 They're going to get wet.
6 He's going to go to bed.
7 They're going to paint the ceiling.
8 They're going to have lunch.

want to

2

b I don't want to
c She wants to
d Does anybody want to
e Do your friends want to
f She wants to
g He doesn't want to/He didn't want to
h Do you want

would like to and *want to*

3 a)

2 Would you like something to drink?
3 My friends and I would like a table near the window, please.
4 Marc doesn't want to stay at home.
5 Which film would you like to see this evening?
6 I'd like to order a taxi, please.
7 We don't want any more coffee, thank you.
8 Would you like to go for a walk in the park?

Future forms

4

b Tomorrow's Saturday ... I'**m** going to stay in bed all day.
c Where do you want **to** go?
d Would you **like** to go out for lunch?
e Chris isn't enjoying his holiday: he **wants** to go home!!
f My friends are going **to** cook a special meal this evening.
g What would you like **to** do tomorrow?
h We **are** not going to have a holiday this year.

Vocabulary
Ways to spend the weekend

5

b a quiet weekend
c a tiring day
d go out
e stay in bed
f always

Word combinations with *go*, *have*, *stay*

6

b a concert, a museum, the gym, an exhibition, the cinema
c in bed, at home
d television, sport
e a novel

Suggestions and offers

7 a)

2 don't want
3 Let's
4 see
5 about
6 could
7 we
8 like
9 idea
10 I'll

Future time expressions

9 a)

9 a.m. Wednesday
this afternoon
tonight
tomorrow morning
tomorrow evening
this weekend
next week
next month
next year

b)

1 tomorrow morning
2 tomorrow evening
3 next week
4 this weekend
5 next month
6 next year
7 this evening/tonight

Talking about the weather

10

b It's sunny.
c It's hot.
d It's foggy.
e It's warm.
f It's cloudy.
g It's snowing.
h It's cold.
i It's windy.

Prepositions

11

b to, c at, d in, e in, f at, g to, h on

Listen and read

12

Chicago	snow, windy	–
San Francisco	heavy rain	–
Queensland	heavy rain	475 mm of rain in five days
Jerez de la Frontera	hot, sunny	30 degrees – hottest so far this year
The Balkans	heavy snow	–
North-east Italy	heavy snow	on Monday and Tuesday
Irkutsk	above zero	first time since last November

Vocabulary
Definitions

13

b vineyard
c gym
d party
e good idea
f let's go
g relatives/relations
h weekend
i meals
j homework
k boring
l look after
m evening
n swim
o concert
p dance
q films
r thirsty

module 13

Present Perfect

1

b has written
c have never been
d has sent
e have seen
f have never driven
g has met
h have never tried

Positive and negative

2 b)

2 has won
3 haven't had
4 has played
5 has never lost
6 has been
7 have played
8 hasn't won
9 has scored
10 has been

Questions and short answers

3 a)

2 Has/Yes, she has.
3 Have/No, they haven't.
4 Has/No, he hasn't.
5 Has/Yes, he has.
6 Have/No, they haven't.
7 Has/No, she hasn't.
8 Has/Yes, she has.

Irregular past participles

4 a)

sleep	S	L	E	P	T			
make			M	A	D	E		
lose		L	O	S	T			
stand			S	T	O	O	D	
speak			S	P	O	K	E	N
take			T	A	K	E	N	
drive			D	R	I	V	E	N
write	W	R	I	T	T	E	N	
say		S	A	I	D			
come				C	O	M	E	
give			G	I	V	E	N	
keep		K	E	P	T			
tell		T	O	L	D			
become			B	E	C	O	M	E
see				S	E	E	N	

Spelling

Regular past participles

5

b ✓
c ✗ tried
d ✓
e ✗ studied
f ✓
g ✗ played
h ✗ lived

ever, *before*, *never*, *always*

6

b always
c ever
d before
e never
f before
g never
h ever

Definite and zero article

7

b the/the
c the
d ø/ø
e ø
f the
g ø
h the

Articles: *a*, *an* and *the*

8 a)

2 a, 3 a, 4 the, 5 a, 6 a, 7 the, 8 the, 9 the, 10 the, 11 The, 12 the, 13 a, 14 the, 15 a, 16 the, 17 the, 18 the, 19 the, 20 The, 21 the, 22 the, 23 the, 24 the, 25 an, 26 the, 27 the, 28 the, 29 The, 30 the, 31 the, 32 the, 33 the

Vocabulary

Ways of communicating

9

b writing a letter
c sending an e-mail
d sending a fax
e buying online
f surfing the Internet
g making a telephone call
h sending a card

Vocabulary booster: the post

10 a)

2 stamps
3 post box
4 postman
5 invitation
6 birthday cards
7 envelope
8 note
9 posting a letter
10 parcel

Pronunciation

Past participles

11 a)

2 gone
3 fed
4 got
5 shown

Improve your writing

Writing a note

12 a)

2 Fiona
3 to the supermarket
4 6 o'clock

b)

Hi Charlotte!
Thanks for feeding cats.
Tins of cat food in cupboard next to window.
Please give one tin ONLY!!
See you on Saturday, about 1.
Love
Tom

module 14

have to, don't have to

1

b doesn't have to
c has to
d has to
e doesn't have to
f has to
g don't have to
h don't have to

2 a)

2 Does he have to use a computer?
No, he doesn't.
3 Does he have to look smart?
Yes, he does.
4 Does George have to fly the plane?
Yes, he does.
5 Does he have to serve food?
No, he doesn't.
6 Does he have to wear a uniform?
Yes, he does.
7 Do Alizia and Meera have to wear a uniform?
No, they don't.
8 Do they have to travel a lot?
No, they don't.

have to, don't have to, can, can't

3 a)

2 can
3 don't have to
4 can
5 have to
6 can
7 have to
8 can't
9 have to
10 can't
11 can
12 can't

Vocabulary
Town facilities

b the art gallery
c the sports stadium
d the shopping centre
e the museum
f the beach
g the park
h the river

5

bridge, castle, directions, end, fantastic, gallery, hill, interesting, journey, kilometre, mountain, necessary, open, park, river, statue, ticket, under, walk.

Prepositions of movement

6

b over
c up
d to
e past
f across
g from
h into

Listen and read
Unusual places to visit

7

	Blue Lagoon	London Bridge	Guggenheim Museums
What it is	a beach	a bridge and shopping/ watersports centre	museum/collection of modern art
Where it is	45 km from Reykjavik, Iceland	Lake Havasu City, Arizona, USA	New York, Italy, Berlin, Bilbao, on the Internet
Why people go there	to swim	to see the bridge, to see the English village, shops and restaurants	to see paintings and other works of art

Vocabulary booster: a shopping centre

8 a)

2 a department store
3 a clothes shop
4 a pushchair
5 a bench
6 automatic doors
7 shoppers
8 steps
9 escalator
10 a shop window

Spelling and pronunciation
Silent letters

9 a)

2 strai**gh**t
3 s**c**enery
4 hi**gh**est
5 b**u**ilding
6 throu**gh**
7 desi**g**n
8 **k**now
9 si**gh**ts
10 ri**gh**t
11 si**g**n
12 lis**t**en

Improve your writing
A postcard

10 a)

2 in
3 great
4 seen
5 tea
6 nearest
7 have
8 English
9 Bye

module 15

Infinitive of purpose

1

b She went to the library to borrow some books.
c She went to the post office to send a parcel to her cousin.
d She went to the hospital to visit her sick friend.
e She went to the greengrocer's to buy some fruit.
f She went to the butcher's to buy some meat.
g She went to *The Oak Tree Café* to have lunch.
h She went to the bus station to catch the bus home.

might, might not

2

2 The plane might arrive late.
3 You might be rich one day, if you work hard.
4 I might not be able to come to class next week.
5 I might not see Frank this weekend.
6 Philip might not stay until the end of the course.
7 The government might change the education system soon.
8 The exam might not be as difficult as you think.

will and *won't (probably)*

3 a)

2 There probably won't be time to stop for lunch.
3 Martha will probably be late for class.
4 You probably won't need your umbrella.
5 I probably won't be able to come tomorrow.
6 There will probably be an election soon.

might (not), *will* and *won't*

4 b)

2 Meg will probably go to Spain with her parents.
3 Sampath probably won't have time for a holiday.
4 Tom might not go to university.
5 Meg will probably go to university next year.
6 Sampath might get a job abroad instead.
7 Tom will probably work for his father's company.
8 Meg will probably become a doctor.
9 Sampath might become an actor.

Infinitives with and without *to*

5

b to get
c be
d to buy
e pass
f to watch
g have

Vocabulary

Education and learning

6

b secondary
c at
d foreign
e doing
f subjects
g take
h pass
i failed
j qualifications
k graduates

7

B Geography
C Information Technology
D History
E Art
F Music
G Science
H Mathematics

Listen and read

8

Picture A = Paragraph 3
Picture B = Paragraph 1
Picture C = Paragraph 4
Picture D = Paragraph 5
Picture E = Paragraph 2

Vocabulary booster: in an Internet café

9 a)

2 desk
3 document
4 printer
5 keyboard
6 screen
7 CD-ROM drive
8 mouse
9 modem
10 scanner

b)

Part of a computer	**Connected to the computer**	**Not connected to the computer**
screen	(modem)	chair
mouse	printer	document
keyboard	scanner	desk
CD-ROM drive		
(modem)		

Improve your writing

Abbreviations on application forms (*Mr, Mrs, Dr, n/a*)

11 a)

Mister	Mr
Doctor	Dr
Number	No
January	Jan
not applicable	n/a
September	Sep
October	Oct
December	Dec
et cetera (= and the others)	etc.

b)

2 e.g. = *exempli gratia* (= for example)
3 kg = kilograms
4 km = kilometres
5 Mon/Tues/Wed/Thurs = Monday, Tuesday, Wednesday, Thursday
6 N/S/E/W = North, South, East, West
7 Pk = Park
8 Rd = Road
9 St = Street
10 tel = telephone
11 UK = United Kingdom
12 USA = United States of America

c)

2 2 kg
3 63 Stamford St
4 irregular verbs, e.g. *bring* and *buy*
5 Queen's Pk Rd
6 London SW7
7 10 km
8 arrived in the UK from the USA
9 tel no: 020 7939 3671
10 classes are on Tues and Thurs
11 Jan–March and April–Sep.

Pearson Education Limited
Edinburgh Gate, Harlow
Essex CM20 2JE, England
and Associated Companies throughout the world.

www.longman.com/cuttingedge

First published 2001
Fifth impression 2003
Set in ITC Stone Informal
and Congress Sans

Page make-up by Gemini Design

Illustrated by Jeff Anderson, Gary Andrews, Kes Hankin (Gemini Design), Connie Jude, Chris Pavely, Mark Vallance (Gemini Design)

Printed in Spain
by Mateu Cromo, S.A. Pinto Madrid

ISBN 0582 403936

The publishers and authors would like to thank Yvonne Gobert and Katherine Stannett for their help and contribution in the development of this Workbook.

Photo acknowledgements

We are grateful to the following for permission to reproduce copyright photographs:

Art Directors and TRIP for 8 bottom left; Corbis for 40 bottom left, 41 middle and 85 middle; Getty One Stone for 65 top, 65 bottom, 68 top right and 68 middle right; Hulton Getty for 41 top and 50 middle; Image Bank for 8 top left; Frank Lane Picture Agency for 65 bottom left, 68 top left, 68 middle left and 68 bottom; Jeff Moore for 8 bottom right; Pearson Education for 49 left (Trevor Clifford) and 49 middle (Peter Lake); Peter Newark's American Pictures for 41 bottom; PA Photos for 5 (all); The Photographers Library for 49 right; Popperfoto for 14, 40 top right, 40 bottom right, 50 top, 50 bottom, 76 and 85 top; Powerstock Zefa for 19; Frank Spooner Pictures for 40 middle right and 85 bottom; Woodfin Camp for 8 top right

Picture research by Liz Moore.